Contents

Grade **4**

S0-AQL-245

Volume **2** Grade **4**

Common Core State Standards

CCSS

Write-in
Literacy Handbook

Mc
Graw
Hill **Education**

Bothell, WA • Chicago, IL • Columbus, OH • New York, NY

Image Credit: **Cover** Wetzel and Company

The *McGraw·Hill* Companies

Education

Copyright © 2013 The McGraw-Hill Companies, Inc.

Send all inquiries to:
McGraw-Hill Education
8787 Orion Place
Columbus, OH 43240

ISBN: 978-0-02-117083-8
MHID: 0-02-117083-5

Printed in the United States of America.

    4 5 6 7 8 9 RHR 16 15 14 13 12

Lesson A
Collaborative Discussions

Working well with other people is one of the most important skills you need in school and on the job. Working with others for a common goal is called collaboration. One way to collaborate is to have a collaborative discussion. In a discussion, you exchange and build on ideas with other people.

In order to have successful discussions, you must sharpen your speaking and listening skills. When speaking, you should be able to express ideas clearly. As you are listening to others, you need to think about what you hear so that you can build on ideas. Then as you discuss ideas, you are able to explore and deepen your understanding of the topic.

In this lesson, you will learn about the process for collaborative discussions, including the following.

● Prepare for Discussions

● Participate in Discussions

● Respond and Build on Ideas

● Reflect on and Revise Ideas

Prepare for Discussions

To prepare for discussions, all participants must do their part and help one another. Being prepared shows responsibility. Before a discussion, follow these guidelines to be prepared:

- **Listen carefully to instructions.**

- **Make sure you understand what you are expected to do.**
  - If you are unsure of the topic of the discussion or what is expected, ask questions. For example, your teacher says the class will discuss the Underground Railroad in two weeks. Each person reads about it before the discussion. To make sure you understand the assignment, you might ask if the teacher could suggest the kinds of books or articles you could read. Write down these suggestions.

- **Plan your time.**
  - Preview what you will be reading.
  - Estimate how much time it will take you to complete the assignment.
  - If the assignment is long, break up the assignment into sections.

- **Stay focused.**
  - Pay attention and stay on task even when it's challenging.
  - To stay focused, set goals and reward yourself with breaks when you reach your goals.

- **Keep track of what you learn.**
  - When reading and studying, take notes. This will help you remember what you read.
  - You can also write down your thoughts and reactions to your reading. You will use your notes when you discuss the material with others.

Now turn to pages 3–4 to practice preparing for a discussion.

Name _____

Prepare for Discussions

Practice

Work with a group to decide how you would prepare for each of these discussion topics. The first one is done for you. Jot down notes about the kinds of planning you would do. Then have the group select one topic and prepare for a discussion on the topic.

Discussion Topic	How would I prepare?
Our Community: Now and In the Past	• Visit the library and talk to a librarian about books on the history of our town. • Interview people who have lived here for a long time. • Read newspapers from the past. Make a map of local businesses. Find out about the history of our school.
Recycling at Home and at School	
Staying Healthy	
The History of Our State	

Name _____

Participate in Discussions

Practice

Discuss the topic that your group chose during Prepare for Discussions (recycling at home and at school, staying healthy, or the history of our state). Use your notes to explain what you learned during your preparation

- Each group member shares what they learned about the topic.
- Write down notes as you listen to others.
- Ask and answer any questions about the information.
- Make connections to the information discussed.

Jot down notes about what you learned from others and the connections group members made during your discussion.

What I Learned from Others	Connections Made

Participate in Discussions

When discussing topics with a partner, a group, or with the whole class, you need to listen carefully and think about the ideas that others are presenting. Then think about how these ideas relate to the information you learned when preparing for the discussion. During a discussion, follow these guidelines:

- Listen carefully to the thoughts of others.
- Review the information that you learned.
- Make connections between what others say and what you say.
- Explore ideas related to the topic.
- If someone does not understand, take time to answer his or her questions.
- Support others who are having difficulty.

Take a Look → Suppose one group read about renewable energy sources. Each member read about a different energy source and was prepared to discuss the topic. The members of the group took turns presenting the different energy sources–solar, wind, and hydropower energy. Then one student added that she read in the newspaper that a local family was using geothermal energy to heat the home. Another student also described another renewable energy source, biomass. The group then compared and contrasted those five types of energy. When you participate in a discussion, there are rules and roles that you should follow.

Rules for Effective Discussions

Follow the basic rules for active listening and speaking when having a discussion. Remember that active listening means paying close attention to what the speaker is saying. You focus on the speaker's message and make sure you understand what is being said. When it is your turn to speak, build on the ideas that others have presented and add your own new ideas. During a discussion, follow these guidelines:

- Sit quietly and look at the person who is talking.

- Pay close attention to what he or she is saying. Take notes if necessary.

- Do not interrupt the speaker. You might miss important information.

- Make eye contact with the speaker.

- Take turns and share your ideas and questions with the group when the speaker is finished talking.

- Respect the opinions of others.

- Be flexible and open to different ideas.

- Make helpful comments.

Take a Look ⇢
Imagine that after carefully listening to what Tanya said during discussion, Aaron did not agree with what she said. Instead of saying, "That's not right," Aaron could say, "I'm not sure that I agree with that idea. Here's what I think." Or he could ask Tanya to explain her ideas more. That way, Aaron is showing respect for Tanya's opinion and is open to different ideas.

Now turn to page 7 to practice using the rules for an effective discussion.

Name _____

Rules for Effective Discussions

Practice

Use this page as an aid to discussion.

Pretend that your group has won a vacation to anywhere in the world. Discuss where you would choose to go. Remember to use active listening skills and be respectful of everyone in your group.

At the end of the discussion, talk with the whole class about how you followed the rules for discussion. If you had any areas that need improvement, explain what you can do differently next time.

Roles for Effective Discussions

Having group discussion roles can help keep discussions on track.
Below are three roles that you may want people in your group to have:

Questioner

- Invites others to ask questions.
- Asks questions to keep everyone involved in the discussion.
- Asks questions to move the discussion forward.

Recorder

- Takes notes on the important ideas that are discussed.
- Summarizes key points and reports back to the class.

Discussion Monitor

- Keeps the group focused on the topic.
- Makes sure everyone gets a chance to talk.
- Reminds group members of the rules for effective discussion.

Take a Look →

Suppose that a student in a group has not shared any ideas. The questioner might ask the student, "What do you think about this idea?" To help keep a discussion going, a questioner could ask, "Are there any other thoughts about this?"

During a discussion, the recorder might miss some of the important information. If this happens, the recorder could say, "Can you slow down and repeat that point?" Or the recorder can ask the group to help summarize the main points.

If the group is getting off topic, the discussion monitor could say, "I think we are losing focus. Let's get back to thinking about this topic." Or if members are interrupting one another, the discussion monitor could say, "Please remember to wait until the other person is finished speaking."

Now turn to page 9 to practice using roles for effective discussions.

Common Core State Standards Literacy Handbook

Name _____

Roles for Effective Discussions

Practice

Use this page as an aid to discussion.

Practice active listening and speaking skills in a group. Discuss which animals make the best pets. Choose a questioner, recorder, and discussion monitor for your group.

After your group discussion, talk with the whole class about how the different roles helped your discussion. Write down notes about how each role kept the discussion on track.

Questioner	Recorder	Discussion Monitor

Respond and Build on Ideas

Communication is a two-way process. That is, speakers and listeners are actively engaged in exploring ideas together. As the speaker presents his or her ideas, the listeners are thinking carefully about what is being said and how they feel about it. When it is their turn to speak, they take into account the ideas that other have presented.

Listening carefully and then asking thoughtful questions makes the discussion worthwhile for all. When you discuss and explore a topic, you develop a greater understanding of that topic. During the discussion, you can make connections, which can help the group come up with better ideas.

Follow these guidelines to respond to and build on the ideas of others:

- Listen carefully and think about what each person says.
- After a person speaks, respond to what has been said.
  - Answer any questions that the speaker asked.
  - Make comments on what the speaker said.
  - Ask questions.

- Build on the remarks of others.
  - When it's your turn to speak, connect to what has been said.
  - Add related ideas.
  - For example, if a speaker discusses ways to work out at a fitness center, you may want to add and compare other ways to exercise, such as dancing or running outdoors.

Take a Look → When you respond to and build on someone else's ideas, you may say something like:

- "I like that idea. Maybe we could also…"

- "I understand what you are saying. I was thinking…"

- "It's not clear to me how you connected those ideas. Can you explain how _____ is related to ____?"

- "I like what you said about…"

- "I would add the idea that…"

Let's say that a group is talking about ways to volunteer in their community. One student mentions that a local food bank provides food for people in need. Once she and her father helped organize the food that was donated. Then another student responds by saying, "When you said that food banks provide food for people in need, that gave me an idea. I wonder if we could organize a food drive at our school. We could ask for donations and deliver them to the food bank."

Now turn to page 12 to practice responding and building on ideas.

5

Name _____

Respond and Build on Ideas

Practice

Use this page as an aid to discussion.

Practice effective communication with a small group. Discuss your favorite hobbies and explain why you like them.

- Take turns speaking.
- Listen respectfully as members of your group are talking.
- Then give feedback on what others have said.

  - Add your own comments.
  - Think about connections to the topic.

Reflect on and Revise Ideas

Group discussions can be a powerful way to gain new understanding. After discussion, it helps to reflect on and revise ideas. Begin by reviewing the main points. During review, everyone should check that all the main ideas are listed. Then members can add their own thoughts and views on the topic.

Here are some points to follow when reflecting on and revising ideas:

- Summarize the main ideas and important points discussed.
  - If you had a recorder take notes, the recorder can read the points that have been written down. Add any other ideas that might have been missed.
  - Include only the most important ideas in the summary.

- Reflect on your own ideas and how they may have changed based on the ideas that others have presented.

- As a group, make connections between the main ideas of the discussion and other things you have read elsewhere, other similar experiences, or something else that you know about the world.

Now turn to page 14 to practice reflecting on and revising ideas.

Name _____

Reflect On and Revise Ideas

Practice

Use this page as an aid to discussion.

In a group, take turns explaining one of your family's traditions. Listen carefully as each person speaks. After everyone has finished sharing, reflect on and discuss what you learned.

- Remember to summarize the main idea and details.
- Add your own thoughts about the topic.
- Discuss connections to the topic.

Lesson B
Listening Skills

Just because you *hear* something doesn't mean you are *listening*. **Listening** involves paying close attention to what the speaker is saying. Listening is active in that you choose to focus on the speaker's message and make sure you understand what is being said. Taking notes, paraphrasing what the speaker said or showed, and thinking critically are important parts of active listening.

Take Notes and Paraphrase

You can have many purposes for listening and viewing. Sometime you want to enjoy your favorite music or a good story. Other times you want to learn something new, such as when you listen to a speaker, a podcast, or view a program on television.

When you need to remember what you listen to, you can help yourself by:

- **Thinking about your purpose** When you know why you are listening or viewing something, you can direct your attention to those parts of the message that are important to you. For example, if you are listening to directions, you pay attention to the order and the details of the steps presented. If you are viewing a documentary, you pay attention to the visuals and any quantitative information it presents.

- **Taking notes as you listen and view** Take notes by writing down only the main ideas and important details. Write words, short phrases, and sentences. Use abbreviations and symbols to help you keep up with the speaker. You don't need to write everything down. Keep track of any questions. Pay special attention to visuals and any charts or graphs presented and include that information in your notes.

- **Using your own words** After the speaker is done, review and paraphrase the information. Review your notes and fill in any missing information. When you restate important ideas in your own words, you are *paraphrasing*. Paraphrasing what you hear helps you better understand the message because you have to say it yourself. It also prevents you from copying the exact words of a speaker or writer when you report them as your own. Copying the exact words of another person and not giving that person credit for them is called *plagiarism*.

Take a Look →

The paragraph below is the information that a listener heard:

Carnivores eat meat. A snake is one example of a carnivore. It eats worms, caterpillars, frogs, mice, fish, and small birds. Omnivores eat both meat and plants. A small bird eats insects, spiders, and the seeds of plants.

These are the notes that the listener took:

- Carnivores eat meat. Example = snake.
- Omnivores eat meat and plants. Example = bird.

This is the paraphrase that the listener made:

Carnivores, like snakes, only eat meat. Omnivores, like birds, eat both meat and plants.

Now turn to pages 17–20 to practice taking notes and paraphrasing different kinds of information.

Name _____

Take Notes and Paraphrase Oral Information

Practice

Use this page as an aid to discussion.

Tell a partner about a book that you read. Have your partner take notes. When you are done speaking, tell your partner to paraphrase the information. Then switch roles. Remember to:

- Write phrases or short sentences when you take notes.

- Review your notes and ask any questions.

- Paraphrase the main points using your own words.

Name _____

Take Notes and Paraphrase Visual Information

Practice

Use this page as an aid to discussion.

With a partner, read aloud the paragraphs and time line. Take notes and then paraphrase the information. Remember to:

- Write phrases or short sentences when you take notes.

- Include information from visuals, such as a time line or flowchart, in your notes.

- Review your notes and ask any questions.

- Paraphrase the main points using your own words.

Frederick Douglass

As a boy in the early 1800s, Frederick Douglass was an enslaved African American. He believed that he had to read and write if he wanted to be free someday, so he made it his goal to get an education. But he faced a big challenge. It was against the law to teach enslaved people how to read.

Young Frederick worked in a place where men built ships. The workers labeled each piece they made with a letter that stood for where the piece would go. By watching the men, Frederick learned to identify and write a few letters.

Over time Frederick learned to write well. When he grew up, he escaped from slavery. He used his powerful writing and speaking skills to fight for human rights. He became famous as an abolitionist, a person who fought to end slavery.

Frederick first met President Lincoln in 1863. Lincoln valued Frederick's opinions and friendship. The Civil war ended in 1865. That year, the Thirteenth Amendment abolished slavery in the United States.

Name _____

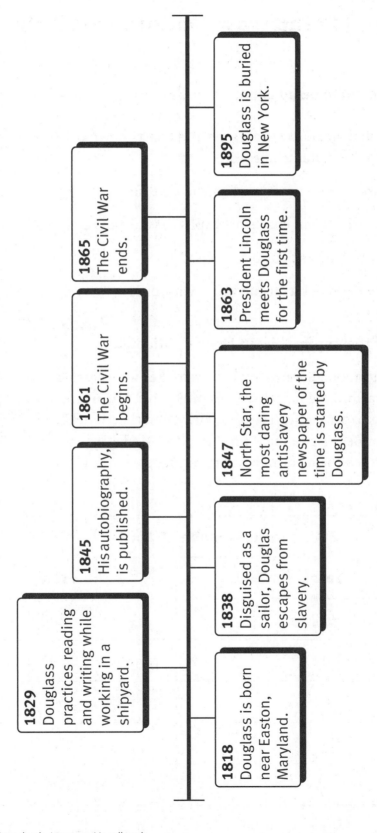

1895 Douglass is buried in New York.

1865 The Civil War ends.

1863 President Lincoln meets Douglass for the first time.

1861 The Civil War begins.

1847 North Star, the most daring antislavery newspaper of the time is started by Douglass.

1845 His autobiography, is published.

1838 Disguised as a sailor, Douglas escapes from slavery.

1829 Douglass practices reading and writing while working in a shipyard.

1818 Douglass is born near Easton, Maryland.

Name _____

Take Notes and Paraphrase Quantitative Information

Practice

Use this page as an aid to discussion.

With a partner, read aloud the paragraph and chart shown below. Take notes and then paraphrase the information. Remember to:

- Write phrases or short sentences when you take notes.

- Include information from charts or graphs in your notes.

- Review your notes and ask any questions.

- Paraphrase the main points using your own words

The Birth of the Automobile in Detroit, Michigan

When automobiles were first invented, they were costly to produce. Few people could afford them. Henry Ford of Detroit, Michigan, found a way to make cars less expensive. In 1908 Ford invented the Model T, a reliable and affordable car. Because he mass-produced the Model T on assembly lines, he was able to sell them cheaply and many people were able to afford them.

Price of a Model T Ford	
Year	**Price**
1911	$780
1912	$690
1913	$600
1914	$550
1915	$360

Think Critically While Listening

When you are listening to a speaker, you need to think about the speaker's message. Speakers often give an idea or opinion about a topic. Speakers then support the idea with **reasons** or **evidence.** Reasons and evidence help a listener understand the topic or viewpoint of the speaker.

To understand what a speaker's main points are, you need to think about what the speaker is saying. Follow these tips.

- Identify the main idea of the speaker.
  - Usually the speaker will explain the main idea at the beginning of the speech. The main idea can also be summarized at the end as well.
  - Ask yourself, "What is the speaker talking about?"

- Identify the purpose of the speech.
  - Ask yourself if the speaker wants to inform, entertain, or persuade the listeners.
  - For example, if a speaker is talking about a state, he may want to inform people about different places to visit in the state, he may want to tell people a story about something that happened in the history of the state, or he may want to persuade people to visit the state.

- Identify the reasons and evidence of the speech.
  - Recognize the reasons and evidence that the speaker uses to support particular points.
  - Speakers will often give reasons that provide a logical explanation that supports their ideas. Good reasons can convince listeners that the speaker's points are true.
  - Speaker will often use evidence that provides proof that their points are valid and true.

Informative Speech: Model

To listen to an audio version of "Water, Water Everywhere," follow the steps below. Then identify the main idea and the reasons and evidence that the speaker gives.

1. Type in your *Common Core State Standards Literacy eHandbook* address in your browser's address bar.

2. Click on Part 5 Speaking and Listening in the first Table of Contents.

3. Go to 5.1 Comprehension and Collaboration in the second Table of Contents.

4. Click on Lesson B Listening Skills

5. Click on Think Critically While Listening.

6. Click on Model.

7. Click on Listen.

Water, Water Everywhere

Water is an important resource in Washington and Oregon. The Pacific Ocean and the Columbia River add greatly to the economies of both states. Freshwater runs through dams on the Columbia River. Water from this river is used for irrigation, power generation, fishing, and recreation.

Water transportation is also important to both states. The harbors on Puget Sound in Washington offer easy access to the ocean. Portland is one of Oregon's most important ports. It is located on the Columbia River. From here ships head to the Pacific Ocean and then to places all over the world.

What is the speaker's main idea?

To find the main idea, ask yourself: *What does the author want to tell me?*

The speaker's **main idea** is underlined in the text below.

Water, Water Everywhere

<u>Water is an important resource in Washington and Oregon.</u>
The Pacific Ocean and the Columbia River add greatly to the
economies of both states. Freshwater runs through dams on
the Columbia River. Water from this river is used for irrigation,
power generation, fishing, and recreation.

Water transportation is also important to both states. The
harbors on Puget Sound in Washington offer easy access to the
ocean. Portland is one of Oregon's most important ports. It is
located on the Columbia River. From here ships head to the
Pacific Ocean and then to places all over the world.

What evidence does the speaker give to support the main idea?

In the first paragraph the speaker talks about how the Columbia River is
important. What evidence does the speaker give to support this point?

The speaker's **reasons and evidence** are underlined in the text below.

Water, Water Everywhere

Water is an important resource in Washington and Oregon.
The Pacific Ocean and the Columbia River add greatly to the
economies of both states. Freshwater runs through dams on
the Columbia River. <u>Water from this river is used for irrigation,
power generation, fishing, and recreation.</u>

Water transportation is also important to both states. The
harbors on Puget Sound in Washington offer easy access to the
ocean. Portland is one of Oregon's most important ports. It is
located on the Columbia River. From here ships head to the
Pacific Ocean and then to places all over the world.

Now turn to page 24 to practice thinking critically while listening.

Name _____

Think Critically While Listening

Practice

Use this page as an aid to discussion.

Think about your favorite activity. Explain to a partner why you like that activity.

- Decide if you want to inform or persuade your partner.

- Remember to state your main idea.

- Include reasons and evidence to support your main idea.

Ask your partner to write down the main idea and details that he or she heard while listening. Check that your partner identified all of your reasons and evidence and discuss any differences. Then switch roles.

Lesson A

Present a Report

Have you ever wondered how people present a research report so easily and with cool features like technology and visuals? This lesson explains how.

A **research report** presents information about a topic using facts, details, descriptions, definitions, quotations, or examples.

To learn about writing a research report, go to 4.3 Lesson A **Writing: Use the Research Process** on Volume 1 page 385.

Below are the steps you can follow to prepare and present a report. In this lesson, you will learn more about these steps, then use this information to give your own report.

- Prepare
- Rehearse
- Present
- Reflect

Prepare

Once you are assigned to present a report, start by taking a look at your written report or a report you have read to prepare your presentation. Then you need to organize the information you will share with your audience. As you prepare your speech, you can also choose to use visuals. Then you should create note cards to help you remember what to say.

Organize Your Presentation

Review your report and decide what information you want to include in your presentation. To help your audience understand and remember your key points, choose only two or three main points. If your presentation has a time limit, that will also affect how much information you can include.

As you are organizing your presentation, remember to consider sequence. Your presentation should have a beginning, middle, and end.

Beginning

The beginning of your presentation should grab the audience's attention. You may want to use one of these methods listed below to start your presentation.

- Place the audience in the center of the action.
- Ask questions.
- Tell a surprising fact.
- Tell a true story.

You will also want to introduce your topic and give your thesis statement. A thesis statement tells what your report is about.

Compare these two models. Which one grabs your attention?

Written Report

In the hot, humid tropical rain forests of Central and South America, poison dart frogs live exotic lives. With their bright colors and their powerful venom, these stunning animals are both friend and foe to humans. Some species are endangered.

Oral Presentation

Imagine that you are in a hot, humid tropical rain forest in Central or South America. You look at a leaf and see a tiny frog that is a bright golden yellow color. You recognize that this is an endangered poison dart frog. What would you think? Would you think that poison dart frogs are friends or foes to humans? In my report I will tell you about the characteristics of poison dart frogs, their toxicity, and how people have used the frogs.

Middle

The middle of your presentation will include more information about or examples of your thesis. Each paragraph can start with a topic sentence and then use facts, details, descriptions, definitions, quotations, and examples to support and explain your thesis. Choose two or three main point or examples.

Make sure to use transitions from one point or example to the next. Transitions are words and phrases that connect sentences and paragraphs. Transition words can do the following:

- show location (*across, around, between*)
- show time (*after, then, during*)
- compare things (*similarly, also, likewise*)
- contrast (*unlike, even though, however*)
- emphasize a point (*for this reason, in fact, again*)
- add information (*next, finally, along with, another*)
- summarize (*in conclusion, lastly, as a result*)

Take a Look → Read the paragraphs below and notice the underlined transition between paragraphs.

The smallest species of poison dart frogs is less than half an inch. That's smaller than the size of a paper clip! Although they are small animals, poison dart frogs are hard to miss. What the frogs lack in size, they make up for with bright, brilliant colors and patterns. Poison dart frogs can be blue, purple, green, red, yellow, or orange. One might think that this bright coloring would attract predators, but it actually warns them to stay away.

In fact, poison dart frogs are among the most toxic animals on Earth. One species has enough venom to kill 10 grown men! Scientists aren't sure where the poison comes from, but they think the frogs take in plant poisons from the ants, termites, and beetles they eat.

End

The conclusion of your presentation includes the main points and reviews your thesis statement. If often helps to look at the opening statements. Look at how you started the report to help you make that connection. For instance, if you started with a thesis statement, you can summarize your points and ask a question that asks your listeners to think about your presentation.

Take a Look → Now think back to imagining yourself in a Central or South American rain forest. You are face to face with a tiny, golden yellow poison dart frog. You know about its characteristics and its toxicity. Its venom could kill you. But you also know that it's an endangered animal and that the poison might be able to be used as medicine. Do you think of the frog as a friend or foe? Has your opinion changed?

Use Visuals

Think about the information you are presenting and decide if any visuals would help your audience. Visuals can help your audience understand and remember the main ideas and key details of your report. The list below shows different types of visuals you may want to use or create.

- **Objects and Models:** Real objects or models can help your audience understand something that may not be familiar to them. For example, if your presentation is about family traditions, you might want to bring in an object that is part of a family tradition, such as a game or traditional clothing.

- **Photographs and Illustrations:** Using photographs or illustrations gives your audience a picture of what you are talking about.

- **Posters:** Using posters can help you show your audience at a glance what the important ideas are.

- **Charts and Graphs:** Using charts and graphs provides a way of presenting facts and data in a simple and organized format.

- **Time Lines:** Time lines can help your audience see at a glance the dates and order of events.

- **Diagrams:** Using diagrams provides a way of showing your audience information with a simple drawing with labels. For example, if your presentation is about race cars, you might want to show a diagram with the parts of the car labeled.

- **Maps:** Viewing maps can help your audience know where the places you have described are.

TIPS FOR USING VISUALS

- Check that your visual is large enough so that everyone can see it.
- Include labels that are short and easy to read.
- Keep the visual simple, and use it to explain one idea.

Take a Look → If you were giving a presentation about poison dart frogs, you could show a photograph of the frogs. To help your audience understand the size of the small frogs, you could show them something that is about the same size, such as a marble.

Use Technology

You might want to consider how you can use technology in your presentation. Technology can be part of your visuals. For example, if your report is about a place, you could show an interactive map. If you want to record your presentation and share it with other classes, you could make a podcast of your presentation. Or if you are reporting about a musician, you may want to play an audio recording of his or her music. Below are some technology formats that you may want to use in your presentation.

- **Video:** Videos provides a way for your audience to watch and listen to information about your research.

- **Audio Recording:** Listening to audio recordings lets your audience hear an example related to your topic. For instance, if you are telling about the first moon landing, you might want to play a clip, or part, of an audio recording of the astronauts.

- **Slide Show:** Using a slide show allows you to display photographs, illustrations, or an outline of important points for your audience.

- **Interactive Map:** Using an interactive map provides a way to show your audience different views of an area. With an interactive map you may be able to zoom in or out. Some programs allow you to add photos, text, or audio, or show landmarks, such as rivers and mountains.

- **Podcast:** Using a podcast is a way to share an audio recording online. If you create a podcast, you can share your presentation with other people at different times.

- **Web Site:** Using a Web site allows you to show your audience additional information, such as images and videos. For example, if you were giving a report on NASA, you might use the NASA Web site to show your audience a photograph of a space shuttle.

- **Multimedia Time Line:** Using a multimedia time line allows you to add images and information to the events on a time line.

/Take a Look → Suppose you are giving a presentation about poison dart frogs, and you find out that your room has access to technology. You might show online videos about poison dart frogs.

Write Note Cards

Once you have decided what information you will present, use note cards to summarize the main ideas in your report. Brief, focused note cards help you remember what to say when you are speaking. When you present, you do not want to read directly from your cards. Follow these tips when writing your notes:

- Write key words and phrases on your note cards.
- Number the cards and put them in order.
- If you are quoting a person or text, write the whole quote.
- If you are presenting facts, write down the fact.
- If you are defining key terms, write down the definition.

Take a Look →
- Frogs are less than half an inch
- Bright colors: blue, purple, green, red, yellow, orange
- Colors warn predators

Rehearse

Practice giving your presentation several times so that you are confident about what you want to say.

- First rehearse on your own in a quiet place.
- Then practice in front of friends or family members.

The more you practice, the easier it will be to remember your speech.

Sometimes speeches have time limits. If this is the case, you should record the time it takes for you to give your presentation.

- If your speech is too short, think about adding information or giving more explanation.
- If your speech is too long, consider taking out some information.

Follow these tips when rehearsing.

- When you present, do not read directly from your notes.
- Make eye contact with your audience.
- Look down briefly at your notes to remind yourself what you want to say next.
- Speak clearly and at a pace that can be understood by your audience.
- If your report has a time limit, time your speech.

Use Your Voice

When you are giving a presentation, it is important to use your voice effectively. It is not just what you say, but how you say it. The volume, pace or speed, and tone of your voice will affect how well people understand you.

- Speak clearly and loud enough for everyone in the room to hear.
- Don't talk too fast. Be sure to speak more slowly when you explain important points.
- Vary your tone of voice so that your speech sounds natural. For example, do not speak in monotone, like a robot! It is okay to speak with excitement about your information.
- Try to avoid saying unnecessary words, such as *um, ah, well*.

Take a Look → Let's say you are listening to a presentation, but the speaker is so quiet you can't hear everything he is saying. He is not using his voice effectively. You might raise your hand and ask him if he can please speak more loudly.

Use Gestures and Body Language

Gestures and body language can help you express your ideas during a presentation. How you use your eyes and hands and position of your body are all important.

- Look at your audience. Make eye contact with them. Pay attention to everyone in the room.

- Gesture with your hands and arms to help explain your points. For example, you might spread your arms out when you are talking about something that's very large.

- Stand up straight and be calm. Avoid rocking back and forth or moving around when it's not necessary.

- Avoid turning your back on your audience. Hold your visual aids beside you so that you can continue to face forward while you present.

Take a Look → The next time you listen to a speech or a presentation, pay attention to the speaker's movements. Notice if he or she uses eye contact. Look at how he or she uses gestures. Does the speaker look comfortable and confident? If so, it will probably be easier for you to listen!

Feedback and Revise

After your rehearsal in front of other people, follow any suggestions that your audience has. They may want you to explain something in more detail or they may give you suggestions about your voice or gestures.

Present

Some people make presenting look easy! How do they do it?

It's understandable if you are nervous. A lot of people feel nervous before they present. So how can you present like a professional? These tips will help you relax and show confidence during your presentation.

- Have all your notes and visuals ready.
- Take a few deep breaths.
- Stand up straight.
- Look at the audience.
- Speak clearly and slowly.
- Speak loud enough so everyone can hear.
- Speak with excitement.
- Use appropriate gestures.
- Hold your visual aids so everyone can see them.
- Remember to smile.

Reflect

After presenting your report, you and your audience can reflect on the information and the speech. At the end of your presentation, you can answer questions from the audience. You can also use comments from the audience and your own thoughts to evaluate the presentation.

Answer Questions

After your presentation, members of the audience can ask you questions about the information you presented. Here are some tips to help you answer their questions.

- After someone from the audience asks a question, repeat it to be sure you understand what is being asked.
- If you don't understand the question, ask the questioner to rephrase it.
- Try to answer the question clearly and briefly. You want to allow time for other questions.
- Don't worry if you don't know the answer. You can offer to research it or ask the audience what they think.

Take a Look → Let's say you gave a speech on poison dart frogs. Someone asks which species of poison dart frogs has the most poison. When you researched the golden poison dart frog, you learned that it is the most poisonous frog. Quickly explain that to the audience. If you do not know an answer to a question, you can offer to research it more and report back later.

Evaluate the Presentation

After your presentation, think about what went well. Ask yourself what areas you could improve upon for next time. You can also ask your peers for feedback on your presentation skills. Write down what areas you need to practice more. Then the next time you give a presentation, you will be more comfortable and confident.

Take a Look → Let's say that after your speech you felt that you talked too quickly because you were nervous. You could write down that to help you feel less nervous, you will rehearse your speech more before presenting. As you rehearse, you will focus on speaking slowly.

Lesson B
Tell a Story

A good **story** entertains its readers and tells about things that happened. Some stories are real and some stories are made up. Writers of fiction use their imagination to create stories. In these stories there are characters that face problems that they need to solve. Some stories are set in familiar places and some stories are set in strange or exotic places. Stories can be funny, entertaining, and informative.

To learn about writing a story, turn to 4.1 Lesson C **Writing: Story** on Volume 1 page 347.

Below are the steps you can follow to tell a story. In this lesson, you will learn more about the steps. Then use this information to tell a story to the class.

- Prepare
- Rehearse
- Present
- Reflect

Prepare

Once you are assigned to tell a story, start by taking a look at a story that you have read or one that you have written to prepare your presentation.

- Review the story and identify the scenes or actions in the story.
- Draw pictures of the different scenes in the story.

Create a Storyboard

Stories are told in a sequence, or order. When you tell your story, you do not have to memorize every word in the story. By breaking up your story into different events, you can remember each important scene in the story.

To help you remember the events in the story, create a storyboard.

- Review the story and identify the scenes or actions in the story.
- Draw pictures of the different scenes in the story.

Take a Look → Look at the sample storyboard about a girl named Mari who competes in a sand sculpture contest. This sample describes what the pictures in the storyboard would be. When you create a storyboard, you would draw pictures of the events.

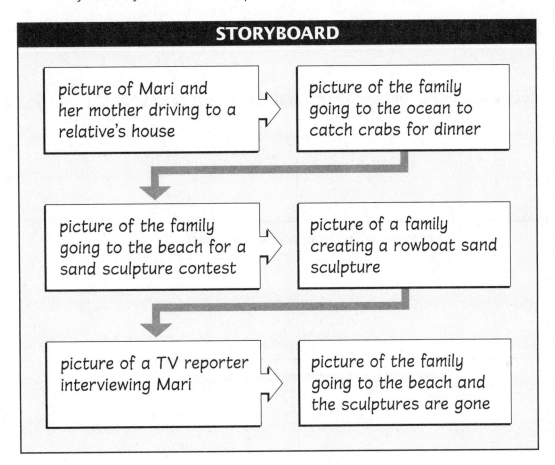

STORYBOARD

picture of Mari and her mother driving to a relative's house

picture of the family going to the ocean to catch crabs for dinner

picture of the family going to the beach for a sand sculpture contest

picture of a family creating a rowboat sand sculpture

picture of a TV reporter interviewing Mari

picture of the family going to the beach and the sculptures are gone

Now turn to page 38 to create your own storyboard.

Storyboard

Practice

Think of a story you'd like to tell and then create your own storyboard.

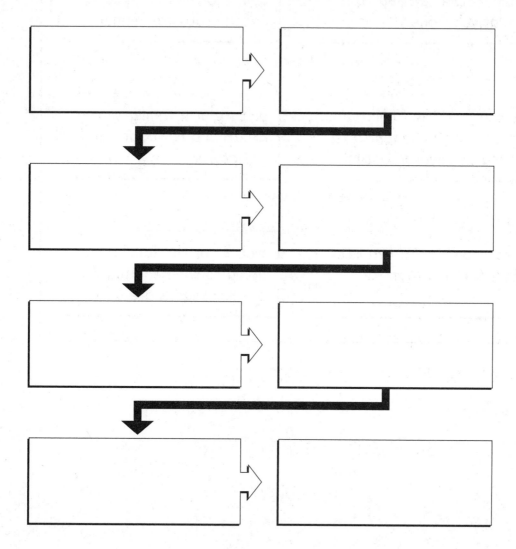

Use Your Voice

When you are telling a story, it is important to use your voice effectively. It is not just what you say, but how you say it. You want your audience to be able to vividly imagine what is happening in the story.

Read through your story and think about the places where you should naturally change your voice. The volume, pace or speed, and expression that you use will affect how well people understand you.

Volume

At some points in the story, you may need to change your volume by speaking louder or softer.

- For example, if a character is telling a secret, you can use a quiet voice for that part of the story.

Pace

Pace is how fast or slow that you speak. Within a story, your pace will change.

- For example, if there is an exciting action that takes place, you could speak faster. To emphasize a point, you could slow down.

Phrasing

When you focus on phrasing, you think about pausing. You may need to pause after a phrase, or group of words. Another time to pause is after you have said something important.

- For example, when you have a short pause, you give your audience a break in the story so they can think about what you just said.

Expression

When you tell a story with expression, your voice changes to show the emotions that a character may be feeling or to add emphasis to something that has happened. You can also use your voice to show the mood of the story.

- For example, if a character is mad, you can use a voice that makes you sound angry.

Take a Look → Suppose that you were going to say the following sentence when you tell your story:

"I am thirsty," Jeremy growled, wishing they could just go home.

You would want to use expression in your voice to show that Jeremy is upset.

Now turn to pages 41–42 to listen and learn about how one storyteller uses her voice to capture the listeners' attention.

Name _____

Use Your Voice

Practice

Directions

Listen to the speaker read the beginning of Chapter Two of "The Birthday Gift." Then answer the questions about the speaker's volume, pace, and expression. Write your answers on the lines on the next page.

1. Type in your *Common Core State Standards Literacy eHandbook* address into your browser's address bar.

2. Click on Part 5 Speaking and Listening in the first Table of Contents.

3. Go to 5.2 Presentation of Knowledge and Ideas in the second Table of Contents.

4. Click on Lesson B Tell a Story.

5. Click on Prepare.

6. Click on Use Your Voice.

7. Click on Practice.

Chapter Two

The Birthday Gift

The day Jake and I turned ten, we finished our daily morning chores, such as feeding the pigs, and heard Grandpa Riley calling from the barn.

When we got to the barn we heard Grandpa call us from the back stall. "Carlotta and Jake," he said, "over here."

Inside stood a young horse, a brown and white pinto colt. His body—even his mane and tail—was dappled with brown and white. A white spot shaped just like a star sat in the middle of his brown forehead.

"What a beautiful horse!" Jake shouted as he reached out to pet him. But the colt threw his head up, out of reach. "Hey!" said Jake. "Hey!"

The colt tossed his head again.

"Soft and low," Grandpa told us.

"Whoa, boy," Jake said quietly. "Good boy." The cold bent his head down and blew softly through his nose.

"Better," said Grandpa. "So, happy birthday, kids. Now get to work!"

Name _____

Listen to the reading again and pay attention to the volume of the speaker's voice.

How is the speaker's volume different when Jake says "Hey," versus when he says "Whoa, boy"? Why does the speaker use a different volume?

_____

_____

Now listen for the speaker's pace. How does the speaker's pace change when she reads, "His body—even his mane and tail—was dappled with brown and white."? Why do you think her pace changes?

_____

_____

Think about the speaker's use of expression. How does the speaker show expression when she says, "'What a beautiful horse!' Jake shouted as he reached out to pet him"?

_____

_____

Use Gestures and Body Language

Gestures and body language can help you engage your audience as you tell a story. The expression on your face, how you use your hands, and the way you move can add to the effect of the story and help your listeners appreciate it more.

Facial Expressions

Your facial expressions can tell a lot about the mood of your story. Use them to express the emotions and thoughts of the characters in your story. A character might have many different emotions, such as surprise, fear, excitement, joy, anger, or happiness.

- For example, if your character is upset, frown or show you are worried.

Hand Movements

You can gesture with your hands to show the emotions or actions of the characters.

- For example, if a character tells his friend to stop, put up your palm to show a stopping hand gesture.

Make sure that you are not using too many gestures, which can be distracting. When you are not making hand gestures, keep your hands down by your sides.

Body Movements

You can also use your whole body to express feelings and action.

- For example, if a character was digging a hole, act like you are digging.

Also think about your posture as you speak. While you should stand up straight, you can change your posture to reflect a character's feelings.

- For example, if a character just ran a long race, bend over and pant to show how tired the character is.

Take a Look → In the story about Mari, you could use hand gestures to show when Mari is creating a rowboat sculpture with her family. When Mari returns to the beach and sees that her family's sculpture is gone, you might say, "Oh no!" and you could frown to show her disappointment.

Use Props

Think about the story you are telling and decide if any props or visuals would make your story more interesting. Props can help your audience understand or relate to what you are talking about. They can also help create a mood for the story. Involving your audience's sense of sight and sound can make your story more memorable. The list below shows different types of props you may want to use or create.

- **Objects or Models:** Use objects or models to show your audience an item that is part of the story. For example, if there is a special toy in the story, you might want to bring in that toy.

- **Costumes:** Costumes can help your audience understand the mood or setting of your story. For example, if your setting is a cold, wintry day, you may want to wear a winter hat, jacket, scarf, or gloves.

- **Music or Sound Effects:** Another way to convey the mood of your story is by using music or sound effects. For example, if your story has someone banging on a door, you could make a banging sound on a desk. Or if your story is about a drummer, you can play a drum to involve the audience's sense of sound.

- **Puppets:** By using puppets, you can help your audience visualize the actions of your characters. For example, if you are telling a fable with different animals as characters, you could create puppets and use them to show how the characters interact.

- **Audio Recording:** Audio recordings let your audience hear an example of a sound in your story. Sounds can also set the mood of the story. For example, if your story has a special sound, such as a bird call, you might want to play a short clip of the sound.

TIPS FOR USING PROPS

- Keep the visuals and other props simple.

- Only use a prop if it makes your story more interesting. Not all stories need props.

- Do not use so many props that it becomes complicated to tell the story.

Take a Look → If you were going to tell Mari's story, you could bring in a bucket of sand or a picture of a rowboat. You could also use a prop, such as a wind-up car if you have one. You could also play a soundtrack of an ocean and seagulls.

Rehearse

Making presentations is not easy for everyone. Some people get nervous and worry about making a mistake. One key to making a good presentation is practice. Plan ahead so you have time to practice your story multiple times. Practice telling your story several times so that you are confident about what you want to say.

- First rehearse on your own in a quiet place.
- Afterward, practice in front of friends or family members.
- The more you practice, the easier it will be to remember your story.

Consider Your Audience

When you tell a story, you are communicating with your audience. You want to make the story interesting and easy for your audience to understand. Here are some tips on using your voice and gestures.

Use Your Voice Effectively

- Speak clearly and loud enough for everyone in the room to hear.
- Don't talk too fast. Be sure to include pauses in your story, especially after funny or important moments.
- Remember to match your volume, pace, and expression to what is happening in the story.
- Try to avoid saying unnecessary words, such as *um, ah, well.*

Use Gestures Effectively

- Use facial expressions, hand gestures, and body movement to help explain your story. For example, you might spread your arms out when you are talking about something that's very large.
- Stand up straight and be calm. Avoid rocking back and forth or moving around when it's not necessary.
- Look at your audience. Make eye contact with them. Pay attention to everyone in the room.
- Avoid turning your back on your audience. If you are using any props, make sure your audience can see or hear them.

5

Take a Look → Suppose you are listening to a story, and the speaker is always moving back and forth. He is not using his gestures effectively because that movement is not helping to tell the story and is distracting. After listening to the story, your feedback to him might be to rehearse his story while standing so that he can practice making meaningful gestures.

Seek Feedback and Revise

After you rehearse in front of other people, ask for feedback. Follow any suggestions that you think will improve your presentation. Your audience may want you to explain a part of your story in more detail or they may give you suggestions about your voice or gestures.

Present

When you give your presentation, make sure that you use your storyboard. If you are using any props, have them ready. Try to relax and be confident. Take a few deep breaths and remember to smile. Follow these tips:

- Stand up straight.
- Look at the audience.
- Speak clearly and slowly.
- Speak loud enough so everyone can hear.
- Speak with expression and vary your pace and the volume of your voice to match what is happening in the story.
- Use appropriate gestures.
- Display any visuals so the audience can see them.

Reflect

After you tell your story, you and your audience can reflect on the presentation and your speaking abilities.

Answer Questions

After your presentation, members of the audience can ask you questions about your story or tell what they liked about the story. Here are some tips to help you answer their questions.

- After someone from the audience asks a question, repeat it to be sure you understand what is being asked.
- If you don't understand, ask the questioner to rephrase the question.
- Try to answer the question clearly and briefly. You want to allow time for other questions.

Take a Look → If someone points out a part of the story that didn't make sense and you are not sure of an answer, you can say that you had not thought about that. You may want to revise your story later to fix that misunderstanding.

Evaluate the Presentation

After your presentation, think about what went well. Ask yourself what areas you could improve upon for next time. You can also ask your peers for feedback on your presentation skills. Remember that your peers want to help you. If they suggest an area that needs improvement, you can work on making that change for your next presentation.

Write down what areas you need to work on. Then the next time you give a presentation, you will be more comfortable and confident.

Answer these questions:

- What went well?
- What do I need to work on?
- What did other people think of my presentation?

Take a Look → Suppose that after your presentation you felt that you needed to rely less on your storyboard. You could write down that area of improvement. Then the next time that you rehearse telling a story, you can focus on repeating the events without using visual aids. With more rehearsals, it will be easier for you to remember the parts of the story. You will also probably feel more confident and prepared.

Lesson C
Recount an Experience

A **personal narrative** is a true story about something that happened in someone's life. When you tell an interesting story about yourself, you are recounting an experience. By sharing an experience, you tell others what happened and how you felt about the experience.

To learn about writing a personal narrative, go to 4.1 Lesson C **Writing: Personal Narrative** on Volume 1 page 319.

Below are the steps you can follow to recount an experience.

- Prepare
- Rehearse
- Present
- Reflect

Prepare

Use a personal narrative that you have written to prepare your presentation. You should choose an experience that you want to share with your audience.

- After selecting your personal narrative, review it and create a storyboard to help you remember the sequence of events.

- As you prepare for your presentation, you should think about how to use your voice and gestures while telling the story. Decide if you want to use any props, such as a memento or object from your experience.

Create a Storyboard

Personal experiences are told in the sequence, or order, that they happened. When you tell your experience to your audience, you do not have to memorize every word from your written narrative. You can break up your story into different events.

To help you remember the parts of the experience, create a storyboard.

- Review the story and identify the different events in the story.
- Draw pictures of the different events.

Review your personal narrative and create a storyboard that shows what happened.

Take a Look → Look at the sample storyboard about an experience planting vegetables in a community garden. This sample describes what the pictures in the storyboard would be. When you create a storyboard, you would draw pictures of the events.

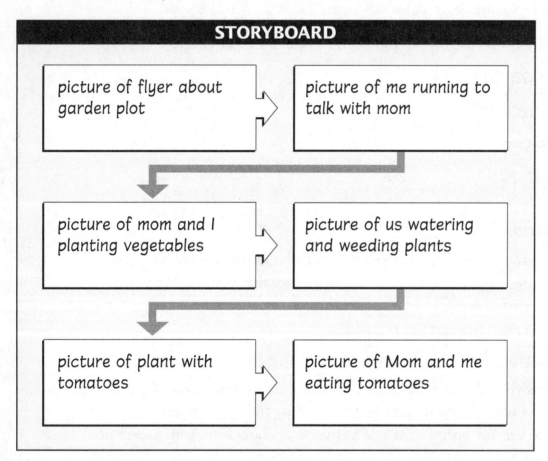

STORYBOARD

picture of flyer about garden plot	picture of me running to talk with mom
picture of mom and I planting vegetables	picture of us watering and weeding plants
picture of plant with tomatoes	picture of Mom and me eating tomatoes

Now turn to page 53 to create your own storyboard.

Name _____

Storyboard

Practice

Think of a experience you'd like to recount and then create your own storyboard.

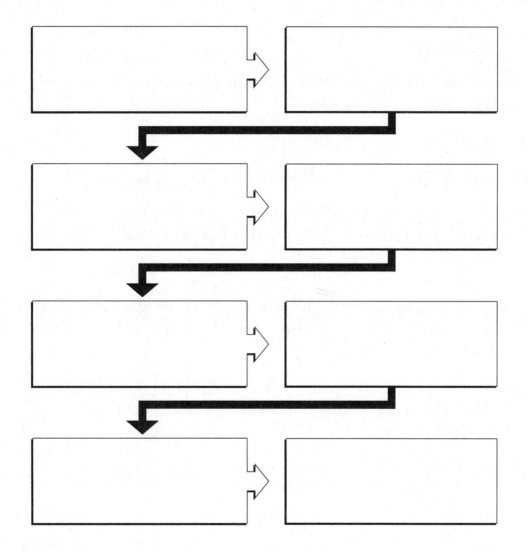

Use Your Voice

When you are recounting an experience, it is important to use your voice effectively. It is not just what you say, but how you say it. As you share your story, you want your audience to feel like they are reliving the experience.

Read through your narrative and think about the places where you should naturally change your voice. The volume, pace or speed, phrasing, and expression that you use will affect how well people understand you.

Volume

At some points in the story, you may need to change your volume by speaking louder or softer.

- For example, if you are describing something exciting that you did, you can speak in a louder voice.

Pace

Pace is how fast or slow that you speak. Within a story, your pace will change.

- For example, if you are describing how you carefully tiptoed across a room as your sister was sleeping, you could speak at a slower pace.

Phrasing

When you focus on phrasing, you think about pausing. You may need to pause after a group of words. Another time to pause is after you have said something important.

- For example, if you just said that you wanted your family to adopt a cat, you can pause. This gives your audience a break so they can think about what you just said.

Expression

When you recount an experience with expression, your voice changes to show the emotions that you felt or to add emphasis to something that happened. You can also use your voice to show the mood of the story. Ask yourself these questions:

- How did I feel about the experience? Was I happy, excited, angry, sad, or worried?
- How should my voice change to show my emotions?

Take a Look → Suppose that you were going to say the following sentence:

"I rushed home and told my mother about the urban garden."

You would want to use expression in your voice to show that you were excited. You could also speak a little faster as you say that you rushed home.

Now turn to pages 56–57 to listen and learn about how one speaker uses her voice to help the audience relive her experience.

Name _____

Use Your Voice

Practice

Directions

Follow the directions to listen to the speaker tell the ending of his experience at a robot competition.

1. Type in your *Common Core State Standards Literacy eHandbook* address into your browser's address bar.

2. Click on Part 5 Speaking and Listening in the first Table of Contents.

3. Go to 5.2 Presentation of Knowledge and Ideas in the second Table of Contents.

4. Click on Lesson C Recount an Experience.

5. Click on Prepare.

6. Click on Use Your Voice.

7. Click on Practice.

Hector was part of a Science Camp and they built a robot for the race. Alyana was a member of the team, but came late because she was at a soccer game.

After listening to the audio, answer the questions about the speaker's volume, pace, and expression. Write your answers on the lines on the next page.

Just as we were lining up the robots, we heard, "Wait for me, guys!" It was Alyana. She was in her muddy soccer uniform, but boy, were we glad to see her!

"We won our championship," Alyana said. "Now let's see if we can win this competition too!"

When the race began, our robot started slowly. But before long it was catching up. In just another ten seconds, it was ahead of all the other robots. And then it crossed the finish line!

It was first! Our robot won the race! We yelled and jumped around and high-fived one another.

Our robot received a special prize for being "Fastest Robot," and we placed second overall. It was one of the most thrilling things I'd ever done. It sure changed my perspective on Science Camp. And better yet, I made some really great friends.

Listen to the speaker again and pay attention to the volume of Hector's voice.

Name _____

How is Hector's volume different when he says, "Wait for my guys!"? Why does he use a different volume?

_____

_____

Now listen for Hector's pace. How does Hector's pace change when he says, "Our robot received a special prize for being 'Fastest Robot,' and we placed second overall"? Why do you think his pace changes?

_____

_____

Think about the speaker's use of expression. How does Hector show expression when he says, "Our robot won the race!"?

_____

_____

Use Gestures and Body Language

Gestures and body language can help you engage your audience as you recount your experience. The expression on your face, how you use your hands, and the way you move can add to the effect of the story and help your listeners appreciate it more.

Facial Expressions

Your facial expressions can tell a lot about your experience. Use your face to express the emotions and thoughts that you had during the experience you are presenting. You may have felt surprised, fearful, excited, joyful, angry, or happy.

- For example, if you are telling about a time that you were shocked, you can show a surprising look on your face.

Hand Movements

Your gestures with your hands can also show your emotions or actions that you took.

- For example, if your experience happened on a hot day, you could use your hands to fan yourself.

Make sure that you are not using too many gestures, which can be distracting. When you aren't making hand gestures, keep your hands down by your sides.

Body Movements

You can also use your whole body to express feelings and action.

- For example, if you were carrying a heavy suitcase, you can act like you are moving it.

Also think about your posture as you speak. While you should stand up straight, you can change your posture to reflect your feelings.

- For example, if you were looking into a dark room, you can bend forward to show that you looked inside.

Take a Look → As you tell about how you planted vegetables, you could use move your body show the different actions you took, such as digging a hole, planting the seeds, pulling weeds, and watering the garden.

Use Props

Think about the experience you are recounting and decide if any props or visuals would make your retelling more interesting. Props can help your audience understand or relate to what you are talking about. They can also help create a mood for recounting your experience. Involving your audience's sense of sight and sound can make your retelling more memorable. The list below shows different types of props you may want to use or create.

- **Objects or Mementos:** Use objects or memento to show your audience an item that was part of your experience. For example, if you are telling about a hiking trip that you took, you could bring in a map of the area.

- **Costumes:** Using costumes can help your audience understand the mood or setting of your experience. For example, if your experience took place at the beach, you may want to wear sunglasses.

- **Music or Sound Effects:** Another way to convey the mood of your story is by using music or sound effects. For example, if your retelling has someone banging on a door, you could make a banging sound on a desk. Or if you are talking about a concert that you were a part of, you can bring in your instrument and play a part of the song.

- **Audio Recording:** Using audio recordings lets your audience hear an example of the sounds you might have heard during your experience. Sounds help set the mood of the experience. For example, if your experience took place on busy city street, you might want to play an audio recording of traffic, sirens, and other city sounds.

- **Slide Show:** Using a slide show allows you to display photographs or illustrations from your experience. If you have photographs from your experience, you might want to show them to the audience.

> **TIPS FOR USING PROPS**
> - Keep the visuals and other props simple.
> - Only use a prop if it makes your experience more realistic. Not all experiences need props.
> - Do not use so many props that it becomes complicated to recount your experience.

Take a Look → If you were going to tell how you and your mother planted a vegetable garden, you could bring in a vegetable that you grew. Or you could bring in a tool that you used while gardening, such as a watering can. You could also bring in a photograph of your garden.

Rehearse

Making presentations is not easy for everyone. Some people get nervous and worry about making a mistake. One key to making a good presentation is practice. So plan ahead so you have time to practice your story multiple times. Practice telling your story several times so that you are confident about what you want to say.

- First rehearse on your own in a quiet place.
- Afterward, practice in front of friends or family members.
- The more you practice, the easier it will be to remember your story.

Consider Your Audience

When you recount an experience, you are communicating with your audience. You want to make the story interesting and easy for your audience to understand.

Use Your Voice Effectively

- Speak clearly and loud enough for everyone in the room to hear.
- Don't talk too fast. Be sure to include pauses in your story, especially after funny or important moments.
- Remember to match your volume, pace, and expression to what is happening in your experience.
- Try to avoid saying unnecessary words, such as *um, ah, well.*

Use Gestures Effectively

- Look at your audience. Make eye contact with them. Pay attention to everyone in the room.

- Use facial expressions, hand gestures, and body movements to help explain your experience. For example, you might spread your arms out when you are talking about something that's very large.

- Stand up straight and be calm. Avoid rocking back and forth or moving around when it's not necessary.

- Avoid turning your back on your audience. If you are using any props, make sure your audience can see or hear them.

Take a Look → Suppose you are listening to a rehearsal, but the speaker is speaking too fast. He is not using his voice effectively because it is hard to understand his story. Your feedback to him might be to slow down as he speaks. As he rehearses again, you can signal him by raising your hand if he starts speaking fast again.

Seek Feedback and Revise

After you rehearse in front of other people, ask for feedback. Follow any suggestions that you think will improve your presentation. Your audience may want you to explain a part of your experience in more detail or they may give you suggestions about your voice or gestures.

Present

When you give your presentation, make sure that you use your storyboard. If you are using any props, have them ready. Try to relax and be confident. Take a few deep breaths and remember to smile. Follow these tips:

- Stand up straight.
- Look at the audience.
- Speak clearly and slowly.
- Speak loud enough so everyone can hear.
- Speak expression and vary your pace and the volume of your voice to match what is happening in your experience.
- Use appropriate gestures.
- Display any visuals so the audience can see them.

Reflect

After you recount your experience, you and your audience can reflect on the presentation and your speaking abilities.

Answer Questions

After your presentation, members of the audience can ask you questions about your experience or tell what they liked about your experience. Here are some tips to help you answer their questions.

- After someone from the audience asks a question, repeat it to be sure you understand what is being asked.

- If you don't understand, ask the questioner to rephrase the question.

- Try to answer the question clearly and briefly. You want to allow time for other questions.

- If you do not know they answer, either explain that you do not know or offer to research the answer.

Take a Look → Suppose that you told the audience about your first time skiing. After your presentation someone asks you when does the ski season start at the hill that you went. If you don't know the answer, you can say that you will try to find out and tell the group later.

Evaluate the Presentation

After your presentation, think about what went well. Ask yourself what areas you could improve upon for next time. You can also ask your peers for feedback on your presentation skills. Remember that your peers want to help you. If they suggest an area that needs improvement, you can work on making that change for your next presentation.

Write down what areas you need to work on. Then the next time you give a presentation, you will be more comfortable and confident.

Answer these questions:

- What went well?
- What do I need to work on?
- What did other people think of my presentation?

Take a Look → Suppose that after your story you felt that you needed to show more expression while speaking. You could write down that area of improvement. Then the next time that you rehearse, you can focus on using your voice. With more rehearsals you will know in which parts you should change your expression.

Lesson D
Levels of Language

We speak and write differently depending on the situation. We adjust our levels of language depending on whom we are talking to and what the occasion is. For example, we use formal English when we are requesting information from a business or someone we don't know. If we are speaking with a friend, we would use informal English.

In this lesson, you will learn more about formal and informal English and when we use them.

Using Formal English

Formal English is used mainly in writing and in some speaking situations. This style of English has a more serious tone and is commonly used in reports, essays, business letters, and conversations with people we may know but are not close friends with.

- Formal English uses more complex vocabulary than informal English. It uses words that you probably wouldn't use in a regular conversation with a friend.

- When formal English is used in writing, sentences are usually longer and more complex than when you are writing to a friend.

- People also use formal English when speaking in formal situations, such as during a job interview or when talking to the principal.

Next is an example from part of a job interview.

job applicant:	Good day, Mrs. Shin. I am happy to meet you after talking on the phone last week.
principal:	Thank you, Ms. Marks. I am glad you could come by today. Let's get started with the interview. Can you tell me more about yourself?
job applicant:	I have a been a high school teacher for three years now. I taught tenth grade social studies. This past summer I moved here to California, which is why I am looking for a new teaching position.
principal:	Can you tell me about the classes you taught? Did you use technology in your lessons?
job applicant:	Yes. I used a lot of online news videos when I taught about current world problems. I also taught students how to do online research.

Now turn to page 66 to practice using formal English.

5

Name _____

Using Formal Language

Practice

Write your answers on the lines below.

Create an announcement for an end-of-year party at your school. Use formal English to create the announcement. The announcement will be made to everyone at your school, including teachers and the principal. Write down what you would say. Then practice giving the announcement to a partner.

_____

_____

_____

_____

_____

_____

_____

_____

_____

_____

_____

_____

_____

_____

_____

_____

_____

_____

Using Informal English

People often use **informal English** when they are speaking to friends and family. People also use informal English when they write e-mails, notes, and letters to people they know.

- When people write informal English, they use everyday vocabulary and sometimes include expressions and slang that is common where they live. For instance, in informal English, a writer might use the word *stuff* to describe something he or she found rather than a specific name.

- Informal English uses often use personal pronouns, such as *I, you,* and *we,* to create a more personal style than formal English. Contractions, such as *it's* instead of *it is,* are also very common.

- When friends and family members call one another on the phone they usually use informal English.

Below is an example of a phone call between friends.

Samantha:	Hi, Tony. How are you?
Anthony:	Hey, Sam. I'm pretty good. I'm so glad you called. I forgot to write down our assignment for social studies. Do you know what pages we're supposed to read?
Samantha:	Yeah. Just a second. Let me go get my notebook. OK. I found it. We're supposed to read pages 56 to 87.
Anthony:	Thanks a lot. Can you call me back tomorrow? I have to read those pages and finish up my science report.
Samantha:	Sure. Good luck getting everything done. I'll call you tomorrow night.

Now turn to page 68 to practice using informal English.

Name _____

Using Informal Language

Practice

Write your answers on the lines below.

Create an announcement for an end-of-year party at your school. Use informal English to create the announcement. Write down what you would tell a friend about the party. Then practice giving the announcement to a partner.

_____

_____

_____

_____

_____

_____

_____

_____

_____

_____

_____

_____

_____

_____

_____

_____

_____

Lesson A
Sentences

When we speak and write we use sentences to express our ideas. Sentences are the building blocks of language and ideas.

Kinds of Sentences

- A **sentence** is a group of words that expresses a complete thought.

> *David returned my baseball cards.*

- A **statement** is a sentence that tells something. It ends with a period. (.) A statement is also called a **declarative sentence**.

> *My favorite food is tacos.*

- A **question** is a sentence that asks something. It ends with a question mark. (**?**) A question is also called an **interrogative sentence**.

> *What is your favorite food?*

- A **command** tells or asks someone to do something. It ends with a period. (.) A command is also called an **imperative sentence**.

> *Order tacos for my lunch.*

- An **exclamation** shows strong feeling. It ends with an exclamation point. (**!**) An exclamation is also called an **exclamatory sentence**.

> *These are the best I have ever tasted!*

- All sentences begin with a capital letter and end with a period, a question mark, or an exclamation point.

> *I like to collect stamps.* (statement)
>
> *What do you like to collect?* (question)
>
> *Show me your collection.* (command)
>
> *Look at all of those stamps!* (exclamation)

Now turn to pages 71–72 to practice identifying kinds of sentences.

Name _____

Kinds of Sentences 1

Practice

Write *statement*, *question*, *command*, or *exclamation* for each sentence below.

1. Did you go for a walk today?

_____

2. Watch your step!

_____

3. Mark and Sally ate at the new restaurant in town.

_____

4. Clean up your room.

_____

5. Someone please help me!

_____

6. I have a lot of homework to do tonight.

_____

7. Where do you think Heather is going?

_____

8. Write your name on the line.

_____

Name _____

Kinds of Sentences 2

Practice

Write each sentence with the correct punctuation.

1. Are you sure you brought your lunch

_____

2. Maybe Jack took it

_____

3. Class, stay in your seats

_____

4. Don't look in the box yet

_____

5. Have you see a stray cat in the building

_____

6. Cats like eating fish

_____

7. I can't believe that cat took the sandwich

_____

8. Do you think we should feed the cat each day

_____

Subjects and Predicates

- The **subject** of a sentence is the person, place, or thing the sentence tells about.

> ***Rob** walked outside.*

- The **complete subject** includes all the words in the subject.

> ***The gray storm clouds** hung overhead.*

- The **simple subject** is the main word in the complete subject. The simple subject is almost always a noun or pronoun.

> *Some **robots** look a lot like people.*

- The **predicate** tells what the subject is, does, or did.

> *The cat **ran.***

- The **complete predicate** includes all the words in the predicate.

> *The dog **ate all of his food.***

- The **simple predicate** is the verb—the action word or words in the complete predicate.

> *Certain birds **make** good pets.*

Now turn to pages 74–76 to practice identifying and writing subjects and predicates.

6

Name _____

Subjects and Predicates 1

Practice

A. Draw a line separating the subject from the predicate in each sentence. Then write the simple subject and the simple predicate on the line.

example: A cactus | stores water. cactus, stores

1. Desert weather is very dry. _____

2. Wood rats in the desert build huge nests. _____

3. The skin of a lizard seals water inside it. _____

4. The mother carried her babies. _____

5. Deserts get cooler at night. _____

B. Write the simple subject and simple predicate in each sentence below.

6. John packed some snacks for his trip.

   Subject: _____ **Predicate:** _____

7. Roadrunners live in the desert.

   Subject: _____ **Predicate:** _____

8. The spider spun a web.

   Subject: _____ **Predicate:** _____

9. Rabbits and coyotes run very fast.

   Subject: _____ **Predicate:** _____

10. The darkness and cool air refresh me at night.

   Subject: _____ **Predicate:** _____

Common Core State Standards Literacy Handbook

Name _____

Subjects and Predicates 2

Practice

Turn these sentence fragments into complete sentences by adding either a subject or a predicate. Write each complete sentence on the line.

1. Are very dry.

_____

2. Live for 200 years!

_____

3. On their field trip, the students.

_____

4. Plants in the deserts.

_____

5. Come out at night.

_____

6. Most spiders.

_____

7. Hungry lizards.

_____

8. Come out during the day.

_____

Name _____

9. Is reading about deserts.

_____

10. Dangerous scorpions.

_____

11. Animals that come out at night.

_____

12. Caught the lizard.

_____

Simple and Compound Sentences

- A **simple sentence** contains one subject and one predicate. It contains one complete thought. It has one independent clause.

> I like soccer.

- Two simple sentences may be joined to form a **compound sentence**, which contains two subjects and two predicates. It contains two complete thoughts. It has two independent clauses joined together.

> Tony cooked dinner.
> Sarah baked a cake.
> Tony cooked dinner, and Sarah baked a cake.

- A **conjunction** is used to combine the two sentences. You can combine two independent clauses by joining them with a **coordinating conjunction**, such as *or*, *but*, or *and*. Use a comma before the conjunction that joins the clauses.

> I want to play in the soccer game.
> My foot is broken.
> I want to play in the soccer game, but my foot is broken.

Now turn to pages 78–79 to practice identifying and writing simple and compound sentences.

6

Name _____

Simple and Compound Sentences 1

Practice

Decide whether each sentence is simple or compound. Write *simple* or *compound* on the line.

1. Some logs are 100 feet long.

_____

2. Rainwater boils, and it turns to steam.

_____

3. Old Faithful is a geyser, and so is Giantess.

_____

4. Boiling water shoots up in geysers.

_____

5. The elks made a long journey.

_____

6. Elks live in the park, and bears do too.

_____

7. Forest fires burn in the park, and they affect millions of acres.

_____

8. My dad likes camping, but my sister does not.

_____

Name _____

Simple and Compound Sentences 2

Practice

Add a comma followed by *and*, *but*, or *or* to combine each pair of simple sentences into one compound sentence.

1. Elks have come back to the park. Wolves have returned, too.

   _____

   _____

2. I would like to visit the park often. I live too far away.

   _____

   _____

3. Visitors like the flowers in the park. They should not pick them.

   _____

   _____

4. You can look at the geysers in the park. You can enjoy the waterfalls instead.

   _____

   _____

5. I love Yellowstone Park. My brother prefers the beach.

   _____

   _____

6. My aunt came with me to the park. She said it was beautiful.

   _____

   _____

Complex Sentences

- A sentence that contains two related ideas joined by a conjunction other than *and*, *but*, or *or* is called a **complex sentence**. Complex sentences have an independent clauses and dependent clauses.

> I took my coat off **as soon as** I got home.

- A **dependent clause** cannot stand alone as a sentence.

> as soon as I got home

- A dependent clause often begins with a conjunction.

> **as soon as** I got home

- Some conjunctions tell *where, when, why, how,* or *under what condition*.

where	when	why	how	although
as	before	because	as if	if
as soon as	after	since	as though	unless

> You should brush your teeth **before** you go to school.

Now turn to pages 81–84 to practice writing complex sentences.

Name _____

Complex Sentences 1

Practice

Combine each pair of sentences using the given conjunction.

1. The night became very dark. A cloud hid the moon. (when)

   _____

   _____

2. Gracie reads books about the moon. She comes home. (as soon as)

   _____

   _____

3. People weigh less on the moon. Gravity is weaker there. (because)

   _____

   _____

4. I've studied stars and planets. I was eight years old. (since)

   _____

   _____

5. I always put on my spacesuit. I leave the ship. (before)

   _____

   _____

Name _____

6. You can't breathe on the moon. You bring an oxygen tank. (unless)

_____

_____

7. Astronauts visited the moon. The moon is over 250,000 miles away. (although)

_____

_____

Name _____

Complex Sentences 2

Practice

To form a complex sentence, combine these ideas using the given conjunction. Be sure that the new sentence makes sense.

1. The astronaut eats his meal. He floats around in the rocket. (as)

   _____

   _____

2. Light leaves a star. It takes thousands of years to reach Earth. (after)

   _____

   _____

3. Eat some freeze-dried snacks. You work at the computer. (while)

   _____

   _____

4. He goes to the library. He reads books about space. (where)

   _____

   _____

5. Mom doesn't want me to come along. It is dangerous. (since)

   _____

   _____

6. Fasten your seatbelts. The ship takes off. (before)

   _____

   _____

Name _____

7. He brought a chunk of moon rock. He came home for the holidays. (when)

_____

_____

_____

8. They watched. The rocket blasted off into space. (as)

_____

_____

Fixing Sentence Fragments

- A **sentence** is a group of words that expresses a complete thought.

> *David returned my baseball cards.*

- A **sentence fragment** is a group of words that is written as a sentence but is missing a subject or predicate. A sentence fragment does not express a complete thought.

> *My most valuable baseball cards.*
> *Sorted them into piles.*

Now turn to page 86–87 to practice fixing sentence fragments.

Name _____

Fixing Sentence Fragments

Practice

Write *sentence* or *fragment* for each group of words. Then write each group of words as a sentence with correct punctuation.

1. the cat feeds her kittens

_____

2. is very hungry today

_____

3. did you bring your lunch

_____

4. don't step on the cat

_____

5. he ate a tuna fish sandwich

_____

6. because he likes tuna fish

_____

7. what else do you think he likes

_____

8. watch out for the cat

_____

Name _____

9. a cabin by the lake

_____

10. mark likes to swim

_____

11. the lake is cold this summer.

_____

12. swam every evening

_____

Fixing Run-on Sentences

- A **run-on sentence** joins together two or more sentences that should be written separately.

> *The boy found the raft the raft floated down the river.*

- You can correct a run-on sentence by separating two complete ideas into two sentences. Each sentence should have a subject and a verb.

> *The boy found the raft.*
> *The raft floated down the river.*

- You can also correct a run-on sentence by rewriting it as a compound or complex sentence.

> *The boy found the raft after it floated down the river.*

Now turn to pages 89–90 to practice fixing run-on sentences.

Name _____

Fixing Run-on Sentences 1

Practice

Correct the run-on sentences by separating them into two sentences. Each sentence should have a subject and a verb.

1. I'm bored at Grandma's house she doesn't have a TV.

_____

2. We're going bird watching you can bring your friend along.

_____

3. The raft floated by he wondered where it came from.

_____

_____

4. The animals are fascinating I will try drawing them.

_____

5. I played with the otters they let me feed them.

_____

6. Grandma found a pearl inside the clam she kept it for years.

_____

_____

7. He draws a picture on the raft he draws well.

_____

8. Grandma loves the river she uses the raft to float on it.

_____

Name _____

Fixing Run-on Sentences 2

Practice

Correct these run-on sentences by rewriting them as compound or complex sentences. Be sure that the new sentence makes sense.

1. I thought the visit would be boring I had a fun time.

   _____

2. I woke up the birds started chirping.

   _____

3. She looked at the drawings wondered who drew them.

   _____

   _____

4. He's never been on a boat he's afraid he'll get seasick.

   _____

   _____

5. Grandma is an artist is carving a bear.

   _____

6. You can go on the raft you must wear a life jacket.

   _____

7. The fawn was trapped I set her free.

   _____

8. We have to be careful the water is deep.

   _____

Combining Sentences

- A **conjunction** is a word that joins words or groups of words.

> and   or   but

- A **compound sentence** contains two sentences that have been joined by a comma and then the conjunction *and*, *or*, or *but*. A compound sentence has two or more independent clauses. Each clause can stand on its own.

> Linda made her bed, **and** then she ate her breakfast.
> We could go back home, **or** we could drive to town.
> The chair is comfortable, **but** I like the sofa better.

- A **compound subject** contains two or more simple subjects that have the same predicate.

> **Margie** went skating.
> **Jo** went skating.
> **Margie and Jo** went skating.

- A **compound predicate** contains two or more simple predicates that have the same subject.

> Margie **unzipped** her jacket.
> Margie **removed** her jacket.
> Margie **unzipped and removed** her jacket.

6

Now turn to pages 92–93 to practice combining sentences.

Name _____

Combining Sentences 1

Practice

Combine each pair of sentences by using a comma and the conjunction
and, *but*, or *or*.

1. Melissa saw a rabbit. It hopped away.

_____

2. Rabbits have long ears. Hares have longer ones.

_____

3. Rabbits eat leafy plants. They also eat fruit.

_____

4. A rabbit's tail is about two inches long. It is covered with a soft fur.

_____

5. A frightened rabbit will sit still. It will dash away quickly.

_____

6. I would like to have a pet rabbit. My mom won't let me get one.

_____

7. There was a rabbit in my yard. My dog scared it away.

_____

8. You can read a book about rabbits. You can read a book about turtles.

_____

Common Core State Standards Literacy Handbook

Name _____

Combining Sentences 2

Practice

Combine sentence pairs by forming a compound subject or a compound predicate.

1. Kate came to the skating rink. Her brother came to the skating rink.

   _____

2. Nathan works at the skating rink. Nathan practices at the skating rink.

   _____

3. He relaxes on Friday night. He watches television on Friday night.

   _____

4. The skating rink opened at 9:00. The bowling alley opened at 9:00.

   _____

5. Frank is sick today. Frank can't come today.

   _____

6. We went to a hockey game. We cheered for our team.

   _____

7. Sam likes eating sandwiches. Sam likes munching on pretzels.

   _____

8. She took her skates off. She went home.

   _____

Standard
1

Lesson B
Nouns

Nouns are words that name people, places, and things. We could not communicate clearly without nouns. Imagine how confusing the world would be if no one or nothing had a name.

In this lesson you will learn more about nouns, including the following.

- **Common and Proper Nouns**
- **Singular and Plural Nouns**
- **Irregular Plural Nouns**
- **Possessive Nouns**
- **Plurals and Possessives**

Common and Proper Nouns

- A **noun** names a person, place, or thing.
- A **common noun** names any person, place, or thing.

> teacher　　　　city　　　　dog

- A **proper noun** names a particular person, place, or thing. A proper noun begins with a capital letter.

> Ms. Brown　　　　San Francisco　　　　Fido

- Some proper nouns contain more than one word. Each important word begins with a capital letter.

> Statue of Liberty　　　　Boston Red Sox

- The name of a day, month, or holiday begins with a capital letter.

> Monday　　　　October　　　　Columbus Day

Now turn to pages 96–97 to practice identifying and writing common and proper nouns.

6

Name _____

Common and Proper Nouns 1
Practice

Underline the common nouns in each sentence. Circle the proper nouns.

1. Baseball is my favorite sport.

2. The pitcher is named Jackie.

3. My father says the New York Yankees are a great team.

4. Listen to the noise of the crowd sitting in the bleachers.

5. Alyssa said the umpire was wrong.

6. Alex and Daniel play baseball in the backyard.

7. My sister uses a wooden bat.

8. Don't throw the ball in the house!

9. The batter has two strikes.

10. John lost his mitt.

11. Your foot has to touch the base.

12. Let's watch the game together.

13. That ball is a foul.

14. Did you bring your cleats?

Name _____

Common and Proper Nouns 2

Practice

Read the list of nouns below. Decide whether each noun is common or proper and write it in the correct column. Capitalize the nouns in the proper column. Then add two of your own common nouns and proper nouns.

independence day	summer	uniform	new york
hank aaron	stadium	ebbets field	july
home plate	jackie robinson	coach	world series
diamond	game	shortstop	ohio

COMMON   **PROPER**

_____   _____

_____   _____

_____   _____

_____   _____

_____   _____

_____   _____

_____   _____

_____   _____

Singular and Plural Nouns

- A **singular noun** names one person, place, or thing.

teacher	city	dog

- A **plural noun** names more than one person, place, or thing.

teachers	cities	dogs

- Add *-s* to form the plural of most singular nouns.

ball–balls	door–doors

- Add *-es* to form the plural of singular nouns that end in *s*, *sh*, *ch*, or *x*.

dress–dresses	sash–sashes
watch–watches	box–boxes

- To form the plural of nouns ending in a consonant and *y*, change *y* to *i* and add *-es*.

baby–babies	berry–berries

- To form the plural of nouns ending in a vowel and *y*, add *-s*.

monkey–monkeys	holiday–holidays

Now turn to pages 99–100 to practice identifying and writing singular and plural nouns.

Name _____

Singular and Plural Nouns 1

Practice

Decide whether each underlined word is a singular or plural noun. Then write *singular* or *plural* on the line.

1. There are no <u>jobs</u> here. _____

2. My family is leaving the <u>country</u>. _____

3. We're going to stay with my <u>grandparents</u> for now. _____

4. Papa sent us a <u>letter</u>. _____

5. He is meeting us at the bus <u>station</u>. _____

6. We're waiting to get our green <u>cards</u>. _____

7. This <u>trip</u> is taking forever! _____

8. It's been <u>weeks</u> since I've seen you. _____

9. The <u>pages</u> of my diary are filling up. _____

10. I miss the <u>park</u> I used to go to. _____

11. I had to sell my <u>bike</u>. _____

12. The <u>apartment</u> is crowded. _____

13. I kept my two <u>parrots</u>. _____

14. We bought some new <u>clothes</u>. _____

15. She received several <u>letters</u>. _____

Name _____

Singular and Plural Nouns 2

Practice

Write the correct plural form of each singular noun shown in parentheses.

1. We saw many (fox) _____ running across the prairie.

2. Many people from other (country) _____ have come to the United States.

3. (Mass) _____ of people traveled to the west in the 1800s.

4. Some travelers keep (diary) _____.

5. Gather a few (branch) _____ so we can build a fire.

6. She caught a rabbit that was hiding in the thick row of (bush) _____.

7. I asked the neighbor's two (boy) _____ to help me milk the cow.

8. Some people used the old trail, but a few found new (pathway) _____.

9. That chest has many (scratch) _____.

10. Please feed the three (baby) _____.

11. We need more (box) _____ than that!

12. I will write two more (page) _____ today.

Irregular Plural Nouns

- Some nouns have special plural forms.

man–men	child–children	goose–geese
mouse–mice	wife–wives	leaf–leaves
ox–oxen	tooth–teeth	life–lives

- A few nouns have the same plural and singular form.

deer (singular)–deer (plural)

fish (singular)–fish (plural)

- To determine whether the noun is singular or plural, look at the rest of the sentence.

We saw a deer on the road. (singular)

All of the deer ran away. (plural)

Now turn to pages 102–104 to practice identifying and writing irregular plural nouns.

6

Name _____

Irregular Plural Nouns 1

Practice

Look in the box below for the plural form of each singular noun. Write it on the line provided.

calves	lice	children	feet	geese
gentlemen	leaves	potatoes	knives	halves
mice	wives	thieves	heroes	tomatoes
lives	men	women	oxen	teeth

1. man _____

2. child _____

3. woman _____

4. life _____

5. calf _____

6. thief _____

7. potato _____

8. goose _____

9. ox _____

10. wife _____

11. foot _____

Name _____

12. hero _____

13. tooth _____

14. gentleman _____

15. knife _____

16. tomato _____

17. mouse _____

18. louse _____

19. leaf _____

20. half _____

Name _____

Irregular Plural Nouns 2

Practice

Read each sentence. Draw a line under the word in parentheses that is the correct plural form.

1. Chinese (factoryes, factories) produced lots of paper.

2. Wheelbarrows, invented in China, were compared to wooden (oxes, oxen).

3. Chinese inventors experimented with magnetism by placing iron (fish, fishes) in water.

4. The first kites floated through the air like (leafs, leaves).

5. I wonder who first realized it's a good idea to brush your (tooths, teeth)?

6. Magicians placed pieces of lodestone into the (bellys, bellies) of wooden turtles.

7. A member of the Chinese court invented a machine to predict (earthquakes, earthquaks).

8. I didn't know the Chinese had made (compassies, compasses).

9. I think of inventors as (heroes, heros).

10. What different (specieses, species) of animals come from China?

11. These inventions have changed many people's (lives, lifes).

12. (Tomatoes, Tomatos) come with the meal.

Possessive Nouns

- A **possessive noun** is a noun that shows who or what owns or has something.

- A **singular possessive noun** is a singular noun that shows ownership.

> The **teacher's** book is on the desk.

- To form the possessive of a singular noun, add an **apostrophe** (') and **-s.**

> student–student's   dog–dog's

- A **plural possessive noun** is a plural noun that shows ownership.

> The **teachers'** lounge is down the hall.

- To form the possessive of a plural noun that ends in **s,** add an **apostrophe** (').

> waiters–waiters'   friends–friends'

- To form the possessive of a plural noun that does not end in **s,** add an **apostrophe** and **-s.** A few nouns have the same plural and singular forms.

> children–children's   teeth–teeth's
> deer–deer's   fish–fish's

Now turn to pages 106–107 to practice writing possessive nouns.

6

Name _____

Possessive Nouns 1

Practice

Write the possessive form of each underlined singular noun.

1. <u>Ben Franklin</u> almanacs are very funny to read. _____

2. The book is the <u>library</u> book, so please return it. _____

3. People rang the <u>church</u> loud bells when there was a fire. _____

4. The <u>inventor</u> fame spread throughout the nation. _____

5. Have you seen <u>Mary</u> bifocals? _____

6. <u>Ben Franklin</u> was one of <u>America</u> best-known citizens. _____

7. This old <u>book</u> pages are torn. _____

8. My <u>doctor</u> advice is to exercise more. _____

9. The key was tied to the <u>kite</u> long string. _____

10. The <u>battery</u> power is running low. _____

11. The <u>lawyer</u> advice was quite helpful. _____

12. One <u>person</u> work is not enough today. _____

13. The <u>car</u> fender is dented. _____

14. I created the <u>office</u> design. _____

Name _____

Possessive Nouns 2

Practice

Write the plural possessive form of each underlined noun.

1. Those <u>experiments</u> purpose was to teach us more about electricity.

   _____

2. For the first time, the post office delivered mail directly to <u>people</u> houses.

   _____

3. The mayor honored the <u>firefighters</u> heroism. _____

4. Electrical <u>charges</u> effects can be dangerous. _____

5. Ben Franklin won several <u>countries</u> respect. _____

6. The church <u>bells</u> ringing woke me. _____

7. Most <u>limes</u> skins are green, but one kind of lime is yellow. _____

8. The <u>children</u> book was very interesting. _____

9. That is the <u>workers</u> break room. _____

10. The <u>bulbs</u> shoots will sprout flowers. _____

11. Twelve <u>sinks</u> drains must be cleaned out. _____

12. The <u>insects</u> habits inspired my work. _____

13. <u>Airplanes</u> tires are fully inflated. _____

14. Those <u>objects</u> tags are missing. _____

Plurals and Possessives

- A **plural noun** names more than one person, place, or thing.

> doctors   parks   papers

- Add **-s** to most nouns to form the plural. Do not use an apostrophe.

> chair–chairs   pencil– pencils

- To form the plural of most nouns that end in *y*, change the *y* to *i* and add *-es*.

> story–stories   country–countries

- A **possessive noun** is a noun that shows who or what owns or has something.

> These are **firefighters'** trucks.

- A **plural possessive noun** is a plural noun that shows ownership.

> The **students'** lockers are down the hall.

- To form the possessive of a plural that ends in **s,** add an apostrophe.

> teachers–teachers'

- To form the possessive of a plural noun that does not end in *s*, add an apostrophe and **-s.** A few nouns have the same plural and singular form.

> people–people's   children–children's

Now turn to pages 109–110 to practice writing plurals and possessives.

Name _____

Plurals and Possessives 1

Practice

Write the plural or the possessive plural form of the noun in the parentheses ( ) on the line provided.

1. The two girls rode their (bike) _____ up the hill.

2. The (snakes) _____ cages are large.

3. (Library) _____ are good places to go to find information.

4. Some of the (books) _____ covers are torn.

5. All of the (librarians) _____ classes are really helpful.

6. The (childrens) _____ section in the library has a lot of good books.

7. I want to look up some (fact) _____ about snakes.

8. I am also checking out a book of short (story) _____.

9. The (snakes) _____ scales feel dry, not slimy.

10. I like to watch television shows about (animal) _____.

11. I read a book about (reptiles) _____ eating habits.

12. My favorite (stop) _____ are nature trails.

13. I found some great wildlife (magazine) _____.

14. We like the (museum) _____ in the city.

Name _____

Plurals and Possessives 2

Practice

Write a plural noun or possessive noun to complete each sentence. Use the singular nouns in the box to help you.

| box | picture | snake | rattle | skin | prairie | book |

1. She carried the noisy _____ from several snakes.

2. When he saw the rattlesnake, he was scared by the _____ sound.

3. I want to find some _____ about animals in the library.

4. This book has words but no _____.

5. This _____ photographs are very interesting.

6. Snakes shed their _____ when they grow.

7. Will you help me open those _____ to see what's inside?

8. A _____ bite may or may not contain poison.

9. Oh no, that _____ lid is moving!

10. Some types of snakes live in fields and _____.

Standard
1

Lesson C
Verbs

A verb tells what the subject of a sentence does or is. Every sentence must have a verb, so it's important to know the different types of verbs and what they do.

Action Verbs

- A **verb** tells what the subject does or is.

> Lisa **jumped** up and down.

- A verb can include more than one word. There may be a main verb and a helping verb.

> We **are driving** to the beach.

- An **action verb** tells what a subject does, did, or will do.

> Dan **walks** home.

Now turn to pages 112–113 to practice identifying and writing action verbs.

6

Name _____

Action Verbs 1

Practice

Read each sentence. Write each verb on the lines provided.

1. The roadrunners race across the empty desert. _____

2. He pauses near the ribbon of highway. _____

3. A car is speeding down the road. _____

4. The passengers look out the window. _____

5. They are staring at the roadrunner. _____

6. The roadrunner is running again. _____

7. A lizard jumps away from the roadrunner. _____

8. The wind is blowing the roadrunner's feathers. _____

9. Two hares hop out of the roadrunner's way. _____

10. The roadrunner shakes its long tail. _____

Name _____

Action Verbs 2

Practice

Read each sentence. Fill in the blank with an action verb.

1. The roadrunner _____ across the highway.

2. The rattlesnake _____ the desert for other animals.

3. The duck _____ in the pond.

4. The mother bird _____ her babies.

5. The lizard _____ along the sidewalk.

6. The rattlesnake _____ for a place to hide.

7. The bee _____ past the snake.

8. The rattlesnake _____ down the rock.

9. He _____ by a cold, shaded area.

10. You _____ the snake with caution.

Verb Tenses

- Verbs have different **tenses**. They can show action in the present, past, or future.

> Susan **rides** her bike. (present)
> Susan **rode** her bike. (past)
> Susan **will ride** her bike. (future)

- A verb in the **present tense** tells about an action or situation that is happening at the moment of speaking or right now.

> Roger **eats** his breakfast.

- A verb in the **past tense** tells about an action that already happened.

> Sarah **asked** to see the book.

- Add -ed to most verbs to show past tense.

> talk–talked   look–looked

- If a verb ends with e, drop the e and add -ed.

> stare–stared   like–liked

- If a verb ends with a consonant and y, change the y to i and add -ed.

> try–tried   spy–spied

- A verb in the **future tense** tells about an action that is going to happen.
- To write about the future, use the helping verb **will**.

> **I will** call you tomorrow.

Now turn to pages 115–116 to practice using different verb tenses.

Name _____

Verb Tenses 1

Practice

Read the sentences below. Underline each verb and tell whether it is in the present, past, or future tense.

1. Aunt Robin hugged my mom. _____

2. Charlie rides his bike to school. _____

3. I will go to the library this afternoon. _____

4. My parents will come to the school play next week. _____

5. We played a new song in music class. _____

6. Elaine buys groceries for her family. _____

7. She works at the bank. _____

8. The teacher talks to the students. _____

9. The chef cooked a delicious meal for the customers. _____

10. Our school will have a talent show in the spring. _____

11. The people danced all night long. _____

12. Lucas practices baseball. _____

Name _____

Verb Tenses 2

Practice

Write the verb in the parentheses ( ) in the past tense.

1. We _____ Martin Luther King, Jr.'s birthday in January. (celebrate)

2. People _____ home from school for the holiday. (stay)

3. The students in our school _____ about Dr. King before the holiday. (learn)

4. We _____ a program of events about Dr. King. (prepare)

5. Today my class _____ a play about his childhood. (perform)

6. James _____ the lead in the show. (play)

7. He _____ his lines before going onstage. (practice)

8. He _____ his Aunt Betty to come to the play. (ask)

9. Our teacher, Mrs. Clark, _____ us good luck before the play started. (wish)

10. We all _____ our best to make the show a success. (try)

Subject-Verb Agreement

- A present-tense verb must agree with the subject of a sentence.

> *The store opens in ten minutes.*

- Add **-s** to most verbs if the subject is singular.

> *My teacher sings wonderful songs.*

- Add **-es** to verbs that end in *s*, *ch*, *sh*, *x*, or *z*.

> *The boy watches his former voice teacher.*

- Do not add *-s* or *-es* if the subject is **plural** or *I* or *you*.

> *They love the new song for the recital.*

Now turn to pages 118–120 to practice subject-verb agreement.

Name _____

Subject-Verb Agreement 1

Practice

Write *agrees* or *does not agree* to show if the verb in parentheses ( ) agrees with the underlined subject. If the verb is incorrect, write the correct verb on the line.

1. The Invention Lab (opens) today. _____

2. Students (create) any kind of gadget they want. _____

3. The lab (contain) interesting building materials. _____

4. I (want) to make a spacecraft. _____

5. These plastic tubes (looks) good for the fuel tanks. _____

6. Evan (draws) a picture of his robot. _____

7. He (collect) some cardboard pieces. _____

8. These rubber bands (connects) the parts. _____

9. Megan (makes) a silly monster. _____

10. She (finds) some interesting shiny paper. _____

Name _____

Subject-Verb Agreement 2

Practice

Write each sentence. Use the correct form of the verb in parentheses ( ).

1. The performance (begin, begins) in a few minutes.

   _____

2. His two sisters (wish, wishes) Milo luck.

   _____

3. Ms. Barone (decide, decides) to make a satellite.

   _____

4. Two other teachers (work, works) together.

   _____

5. Silvia (brush, brushes) the dust away.

   _____

6. She (build, builds) a space shuttle.

   _____

7. My spacecraft (need, needs) solar panels.

   _____

8. These wood chips (look, looks) pretty good.

   _____

Name _____

9. My dad (wash, washes) off the piece of wood.

_____

10. He (like, likes) to build things, too.

_____

11. We (know, knows) about making things.

_____

12. Shannon (watch, watches) me work on my project.

_____

Common Core State Standards Literacy Handbook

Main and Helping Verbs

- The **main verb** in a sentence shows what the subject does or is.

> I **talked** to Grandpa.

- A **helping verb** helps the main verb show an action or make a statement.

> I **am** talking to Grandpa.

- *Have*, *has*, *had*, *is*, *are*, *am*, *was*, *were*, and *will* are helping verbs.

> I **have** talked to Grandpa.

- *Is*, *are*, *am*, *was*, and *were* can be used with a main verb ending in *-ing*.

> Mom **is talking** to Grandpa.
> Mom **was talking** to Grandpa.

- *Will* is a helping verb used to show an action in the future.

> I **will buy** those shoes.

Now turn to pages 122–123 to practice identifying and writing main and helping verbs.

6

Name _____

Main and Helping Verbs 1
Practice

Draw one line under each helping verb. Draw two lines under each main verb.

1. Gidget always has liked to help others.

2. Next year, she will volunteer at the homeless shelter.

3. The shelter workers have decided to train student volunteers.

4. Gidget has considered other ways to help.

5. She is starting her own group.

6. Gidget and her group are collecting things for homeless kids.

7. As of last week, they had gathered jackets, school supplies, and backpacks.

8. I am thinking of joining the group.

9. Yesterday we were talking about the group.

10. My friends will definitely help, too.

Name _____

Main and Helping Verbs 2

Practice

Write a main verb or helping verb to complete each sentence.

1. Charlie _____ searched for a place to volunteer.

2. He has _____ lists of groups.

3. Charlie _____ worrying about choosing the right place to help.

4. He _____ visit different groups.

5. The people in the soup kitchen are _____ vegetables.

6. Many people _____ donated clothes to this group.

7. This afternoon Charlie is _____ for people who couldn't leave their homes.

8. He has _____ floors at the animal shelter.

9. Charlie _____ pitch in wherever he can.

10. The leaders of the groups are _____ him and telling him he's done a great job.

More Verb Tenses

- The **progressive** form of the **present tense** describes an ongoing action that is happening at the same time the statement is written. This tense is formed by using *am*, *is*, or *are* with the verb form ending in *-ing*.

> The reporter **is asking** the president questions.

- The **progressive** form of the **past tense** describes an ongoing action in the past. This tense is formed by using *was* or *were* with the verb form ending in *-ing*.

> We were watching a movie on television when the power failure happened.

- The **progressive** form of the **future tense** describes an ongoing or continuous action that will take place in the future. This tense is formed by using *will be* or *shall be* with the verb form ending in *-ing*.

> The nurse **will be examining** patients this afternoon.

Now turn to pages 125–126 to practice identifying and writing more verb tenses.

Name _____

More Verb Tenses 1

Practice

Underline the progressive form of verbs in the sentences below.

1. George was helping Roger clean up the mess.

2. They are going to see a play tonight.

3. I will be going to soccer practice next weekend.

4. The waiter was explaining the dinner specials when Ann sat down at the table.

5. The fisherman is reeling in a huge fish.

6. Gabe and Kim were riding their bikes when it started to rain.

7. The scientist will be talking about her research at the next meeting.

8. The students are thinking of entering the talent show.

9. I will be traveling in Europe next summer.

10. The fans were cheering for the athlete when he fell.

Name _____

More Verb Tenses 2

Practice

Underline each verb and tell whether it is present progressive, past progressive, or future progressive.

1. I was talking on the phone when the doorbell rang. _____

2. The florist is arranging beautiful flowers in a large vase. _____

3. Richard will be running in a marathon for the next six hours. _____

4. I will be turning another year older next week. _____

5. The tour guide is telling us about the different landmarks in the area.

_____

6. Emory was mowing the lawn when I got to his house. _____

7. David and Jenny were studying for their test this morning. _____

8. I am going to the dance with a friend. _____

9. Sally and Mike are not talking to each other right now. _____

10. The lawyers were discussing the case when the judge walked into the courtroom.

_____

Special Helping Verbs

- A **helping verb** helps the main verb show an action or make a statement.

> **I am** going home.

- The helping verb can is used to express the ability to do something.

> I **can** swim very well.
> Taylor **cannot** swim.

- The helping verb *can* is also used to the express the possibility to do something.

> We **can** go to the beach this weekend.

- The helping verb *may* is used for permissions.

> You **may** borrow my book.

- The helping verb *may* is also used to express probability or prediction.

> They **may** come with us tomorrow.

- The helping verb *must* is used for strong obligations or duties.

> You **must** finish your homework.

Now turn to page 128 to practice using special helping verbs.

Name _____

Special Helping Verbs

Practice

Circle the correct helping verb in each sentence below.

1. You (may/can) have another piece of pizza.

2. Phil (can/must) play the guitar well.

3. (Must/May) I take your plate?

4. You (can/must) finish your dinner before you go outside to play.

5. I'm not sure, but my sister (may/can) come with us tomorrow night.

6. Terrence and Claire (must/can) turn in their permissions forms if they want to go on the field trip.

7. You (may/must) want to bring a jacket in case it gets cold.

8. Not all dogs (may/can) swim well.

9. You (must/may) bring your passport when you leave the country.

10. My grandmother (can/must) sew all types of clothes.

Irregular Verbs

• An **irregular verb** is a verb that does not add -ed to form the past tense.

Present Tense	Past Tense
teach	taught
find	found
grow	grew
begin	began
blow	blew
see	saw
make	made
fly	flew
break	broke
choose	chose
leave	left
make	made
come	came
go	went
do	did
lead	led
draw	drew
know	knew
keep	kept

6

- The verbs *be* and *have* also have irregular spellings for the present and past tenses.

Present Tense	Past Tense
am, is, are	was, were
has, have	had

- Some irregular verbs have special spellings when used with the helping verbs *have*, *has*, or *had*.

We **have taken** a lot of pictures.

Now turn to pages 131–132 to practice using irregular verbs.

Name _____

Irregular Verbs 1

Practice

Write the correct past-tense form of the underlined verb on the line provided.

1. The snow <u>begin</u> _____ to fall.

2. The sunlight <u>make</u> _____ the snow and ice glitter.

3. An icicle <u>break</u> _____ off of the roof.

4. I <u>find</u> _____ the icicle on the ground.

5. The first snow <u>come</u> _____ earlier than usual this year.

6. We <u>go</u> _____ to the pond to ice-skate.

7. Elijah and I <u>do</u> _____ leaps, twists, and turns on the ice.

8. He <u>fly</u> _____ through the air and landed safely on the blades of his skates.

9. Nina <u>draw</u> _____ a picture of the frozen pond.

10. We decided to go home when we <u>see</u> _____ it was getting dark.

Name _____

Irregular Verbs 2

Practice

Rewrite each sentence with the correct past-tense form of the underlined verb.

1. We <u>go</u> outside an hour ago.

   _____

2. It <u>grow</u> colder after we went outside.

   _____

3. I <u>know</u> it was a good idea to wear my gloves, hat, and scarf.

   _____

4. The snow and ice <u>leave</u> the trees glistening and white.

   _____

5. The path <u>lead</u> us straight to the forest.

   _____

6. I <u>keep</u> my hands in my pockets.

   _____

7. We <u>choose</u> the first day of winter to take pictures of the forest.

   _____

8. The winds <u>blow</u> drifts of snow against the bare trees.

   _____

Lesson D
Pronouns

Pronouns are words that take the place of one or more nouns. There are different types of pronouns that should be used in different situations.

Pronouns and Antecedents

- A **pronoun** is a word that takes the place of one or more nouns.

> *Sarah likes orange juice.*
> ***She** likes orange juice.*

- A pronoun must match its antecedent, or the noun it refers to. A singular pronoun takes the place of a singular noun. A plural pronoun takes the place of plural noun. A pronoun must also match the gender of a noun, which can be male, female, or neither. *He* and *him* refer to males. *She* and *her* refer to females.

> **Singular pronouns:** *I, you, he, she, it, me, him, her*
> > ***My father** talked to **my mother** about the trip.*
> > ***He** talked to **her** about the trip.*
> **Plural pronouns:** *we, you, they, us, them*
> > ***Alyssa and Carla** bought **tickets**.*
> > ***They** bought **them**.*

- **Reflexive pronouns** are used when the subject of a sentence and the object of the verb are the same. The words *myself, yourself, himself, herself, ourselves, yourselves,* and *themselves,* are reflexive pronouns.

> *I trusted **myself** to take only what I needed.*
> *John helped **himself** to a second piece of pie.*

Now turn to pages 134–135 to practice writing pronouns and antecedents.

Name _____

Pronouns and Antecedents 1

Practice

Write the pronoun that correctly replaces the underlined noun in each sentence.

1. At first, Roy didn't want to go to the nursing home because <u>Roy</u> thought the place was boring. _____

2. Mrs. Allen said <u>Mrs. Allen</u> found out that dogs were allowed in the nursing home. _____

3. Roy knew Grandpa would be happy to see Buddy, so Roy decided to bring <u>Buddy</u>. _____

4. The receptionist at the nursing home said to Roy, "I see <u>Roy</u> brought a friend today." _____

5. Mrs. Allen said, "<u>Mrs. Allen</u> got Buddy's medical records this morning." _____

6. Grandpa said, "I'm glad you brought Buddy to <u>Grandpa</u>." _____

7. Grandpa asked Martha if <u>Martha</u> could bring Buddy to the nursing home. _____

8. Another man saw Buddy and said he had a dog that looked like <u>Buddy</u>. _____

9. The man said he had a picture of his dog and went to his room to get <u>the picture</u>. _____

10. Roy threw the ball to Buddy so <u>Buddy</u> could fetch it. _____

Name _____

Pronouns and Antecedents 2

Practice

Write the pronoun that correctly completes each sentence.

1. I said, "_____ think I must take my cat to the vet."

2. I took the leash because I would need _____ to hold the dog.

3. I am brushing my dog Trixie's coat because _____ will be in a show tomorrow.

4. My dog Edward needs medicine. I give it to _____ every morning.

6. Fido buried his bone in the yard, but now he can't find _____.

7. My sister and _____ threw the stick, and our dog brought it back to us.

8. Fran's mother told us that _____ had a cat when she was little.

9. My cousins called, and _____ told me their cat just had kittens.

10. My little brother wanted to feed the dog, so _____ showed him how to do it.

Subject and Object Pronouns

• Use a **subject pronoun** as the subject of a sentence or to replace a noun that follows a form of the verb *to be*. The pronouns *I, you, he, she, it, we,* and *they* are subject pronouns.

> **We** went to the museum.
>
> The guilty person was **she.**

• Use an **object pronoun** after an action verb or after a preposition, such as *for, at, of, with,* or *to.* The pronouns *me, you, him, her, it, us,* and *them* are object pronouns.

> The coach helped **him** with his hitting.
>
> Stacey threw the ball at **me.**

Now turn to pages 137–138 to practice identifying and writing subject and object pronouns.

Name _____

Subject and Object Pronouns 1

Practice

Underline the incorrect pronouns and write the correct pronouns on the line.

1. The villagers loved the man, and them all missed him when he died. _____

2. Everyday when the man woke, him went to work in his garden. _____

3. Her and me went to the well for water. _____

4. Us are the only ones who really know him. _____

5. Them are the people we met last year. _____

6. The young man feared the blind man would be unkind to he. _____

7. Her grandmother saved she from the villain. _____

8. This is a secret between you and I. _____

9. The bugs are a bother to she and Grandpa. _____

10. My father handed the hammer to I. _____

11. Don't forget we. _____

Name _____

Subject and Object Pronouns 2

Practice

Read the sentences below. Then write the correct pronouns on the lines provided to complete each sentence.

1. My brother and _____ saw a blind woman walking down the street.

2. _____ was using a cane to find her way.

3. When people saw _____, they moved over to let her pass.

4. How does the woman know where _____ is going?

5. It might be hard for _____ to run errands.

6. He told _____ that she might count the steps to her destination.

7. My brother asked _____ where I went last night.

8. I told _____ that I was at rehearsal for the school play.

9. Have _____ ever performed in a school play?

10. All of the band members wear the same shirt, which makes it hard to

    tell _____ apart.

11. Do _____ have some extra money?

12. _____ gave my brother some change.

13. _____ could smell the hot dog stand around the corner.

14. This was going to be a good day for _____.

Common Core State Standards Literacy Handbook

Reflexive Pronouns

Use a **reflexive pronoun** instead of an object pronoun if the subject of the sentence is doing the action himself or herself. The pronouns *myself, yourself, himself, herself, itself, ourselves,* and *yourselves* are reflexive pronouns.

> You can look at **yourself** in the mirror.

Now turn to page 140 to practice using reflexive pronouns.

Name _____

Reflexive Pronouns

Practice

Fill in the blanks in the sentences below with the correct reflexive pronoun.

1. Be careful and don't hurt _____.

2. After I go swimming, I dry _____ with a towel.

3. Your baby sister can't feed _____.

4. He made _____ dizzy by spinning around and around.

5. Let's give _____ a break and try again later.

6. The bird washed _____ in the puddle.

7. Boys, please get _____ ready for dinner.

8. The gardener shut the door and he locked _____ in the shed.

9. My grandfather almost fell, but he caught _____.

10. Look at _____! You're covered in mud!

11. I tried to reach the towel _____.

12. He looked at _____ in the mirror.

13. We can plant that tree _____.

14. My sister cannot dress _____ without some help.

15. You can help _____ to some cookies.

Pronoun-Verb Agreement

- A **present-tense** verb must agree with its **subject pronoun**.

> She **makes** clay pots.

- Add **-s** or **-es** to most action verbs when you use the pronouns *he*, *she*, and *it*.

> He **reads** books about dinosaurs.
>
> She **dances** with her friends.

- Do not add **-s** or **-es** to an action verb in the present tense when you use the pronouns *I*, *we*, *you*, and *they*.

> We **read** books about dinosaurs.
>
> They **dance** with their friends.

- The verbs **have** and **be** have special forms in the present tense.

> **Have**
>
> | | |
> |---|---|
> | I have | We have |
> | You have | You have |
> | He/She/It has | They have |

> **Be**
>
> | | |
> |---|---|
> | I am | We are |
> | You are | You are |
> | He/She/It is | They are |

Now turn to pages 142–143 to practice pronoun-verb agreement.

6

Name _____

Pronoun-Verb Agreement 1

Practice

Write the correct form of the underlined action verb to complete each sentence.

1. It <u>use</u> _____ less gas than yours.

2. They <u>makes</u> _____ energy from the wind.

3. Every few years she <u>buy</u> _____ a new truck.

4. They <u>pollutes</u> _____ the environment.

5. Scientists help people because they <u>looks</u> _____ for new ways to make energy.

6. She <u>put</u> _____ up solar panels at her job.

7. She also <u>design</u> _____ hybrid cars.

8. He <u>know</u> _____ a great deal about electricity.

9. Where I live, we <u>gets</u> _____ energy from the river.

10. He <u>work</u> _____ in an oil field.

11. He <u>ride</u> _____ a bike to work.

12. When coal burns, it <u>send</u> _____ soot into the air.

13. We <u>needs</u> _____ more twigs to start the fire.

14. You <u>hikes</u> _____ in the mountains.

Name _____

Pronoun-Verb Agreement 2

Practice

Write the correct form of the underlined verb to complete each sentence.

1. I <u>has</u> _____ a way to tell which house is yours.

2. Your house <u>have</u> _____ six solar panels on its roof.

3. We <u>has</u> _____ had them since last year.

4. They <u>be</u> _____ helping us save energy.

5. They <u>has</u> _____ already saved us some money.

6. I <u>be</u> _____ trying to get my friends to use solar panels.

7. I think Fred and Elliot <u>be</u> _____ going to buy some.

8. Bill <u>be</u> _____ helping protect the environment.

9. You <u>is</u> _____ good with tools.

10. She <u>have</u> _____ a big truck that she uses on the job.

11. We <u>be</u> _____ building an addition to our house.

12. Dad <u>have</u> _____ to nail the beams.

13. We <u>be</u> _____ putting in two windows.

14. Now you <u>has</u> _____ a good design.

Possessive Pronouns

- A **possessive pronoun** takes the place of a possessive noun. It shows who or what owns something.

> This is **Jack's** house.
>
> This is **his** house.

- Some possessive pronouns are used before nouns (*my, your, his, her, its, our, their*).

> That is **the girls'** favorite movie.
>
> That is **their** favorite movie.

- Some possessive pronouns can stand alone (*mine, yours, his, hers, its, ours, theirs*).

> That backpack is **yours**.

Now turn to pages 145–147 to practice writing possessive pronouns.

Name _____

Possessive Pronouns 1

Practice

Rewrite the underlined parts of the sentences using possessive pronouns and nouns.

1. Adelina's father works on a boat, and <u>the grandfather of Adelina</u> does, too.

_____

2. The houses in <u>Adelina's</u> village are small.

_____

3. The village is busy, and <u>the village's</u> visitors come from all over the world.

_____

4. <u>Her family's</u> job is to take people to see the whales.

_____

5. The whales come to the village to have <u>the whales'</u> babies.

_____

6. Adelina's grandfather's stories are fascinating, and <u>the grandfather's</u> job is, too.

_____

7. If you go to Adelina's village, be sure to bring <u>the camera that belongs to you</u>.

_____

Name _____

8. Robert learned about La Laguna from <u>Robert's</u> friend Melissa.

_____

9. Robert and I went there for <u>the vacation we had</u> last winter.

_____

10. I took a lot of pictures for <u>the photo album that belongs to me</u>.

_____

Name _____

Possessive Pronouns 2

Practice

In each sentence, replace the underlined, incorrect possessive pronoun with the correct one on the line provided.

1. That is your boat, but this one is <u>my's</u>. _____

2. <u>Your's</u> is the smaller life-vest, the blue one. _____

3. I don't have my own, but my brother let me use <u>he's</u>. _____

4. You have your oars. Where are <u>my</u>? _____

5. I wanted to ask Mercedes if I could use <u>her's</u>, but she wasn't at home. _____

6. We are off, and the whole day is <u>our</u>! _____

7. Paco and Pepe say this beach is <u>they's</u>, but it's not. _____

8. I forgot my lunch, so will you share <u>your</u>? _____

9. Is that cooler <u>her's</u>? _____

10. The fishing shack on the right is <u>he's</u>. _____

11. Should we go to his fishing shack or <u>your</u>? _____

12. That tackle box is not <u>our</u>. _____

13. <u>It's</u> handle is broken. _____

14. That pretty hat is <u>my</u>. _____

15. Those shoes are <u>her's</u>. _____

Relative Pronouns

- A **relative pronoun** introduces a part of a sentence, or a clause, that describes a noun.

> This is the dress that I wore to the party.

- A relative pronoun *relates* to another noun that comes before it in a sentence. There are five main relative pronouns: *that, which, who, whom* and *whose*.

> Benjamin Banneker wrote an almanac **that** contained important information.

- Use *that* when the relative pronoun relates to information that is necessary to the reader's understanding of the sentence. Do not use a comma with *that*.

> The place **that** we visited is the beautiful Crater Lake.

- Use *which* when the relative pronoun relates to information that is not essential to understand the sentence. Use a comma before *which*.

> Crater Lake National Park, which is 249 square miles, is a beautiful place to visit.

- Use *who* when the relative pronoun relates to the subject of the clause. If you can substitute the relative pronoun with the personal pronoun *he* or *she*, use the relative pronoun *who*.

> Joyce is the girl **who** got the job.
> She got the job.

- Use *whom* when the relative pronoun relates to the object of the clause. If you can substitute the relative pronoun with the personal pronoun *him* or *her*, use the relative pronoun *whom*.

> Jim is the person with **whom** I went fishing last spring.
>
> I went fishing with him.

- Use *whose* when the relative pronoun is possessive. The relative pronoun *whose* can refer to both people and things.

> The family **whose** dog ran away was very upset.
>
> The book **whose** author won an award has become a bestseller.

Now turn to page 150 to practice using relative pronouns.

6

Name _____

Relative Pronouns

Practice

Circle the correct relative pronoun in parentheses.

1. Tara, Tara is the television show (that/who) won all those awards.

2. Ingrid James is the actress (who/whom) stars on the show.

3. Paul Wright is the character (who/whose) I said was my favorite.

4. Jade Cleese is the actress (whom/whose) autograph I got today.

5. Do you still have the magazine (that/which) you read about the actors?

6. Mark is the person with (who/whom) I discussed the television show.

7. The actress wore diamonds, (that/which) are expensive.

8. I don't know (who/whom) I like better.

9. All of the jewelry (that/which) she wore sparkled.

10. The actress (whose/who) movie was popular was given an award.

Pronouns and Homophones

Homophones are words that sound alike but have different spellings and meanings.

Their, they're, and *there* are homophones that are often confused.

> *Their* is a possessive pronoun that shows ownership.
>> *We stopped at **their** house.*
>
> *They're* is a contraction for *they are.*
>> *We hope that **they're** coming soon.*
>
> *There* is a pronoun that tells where something is.
>> *We put the package over **there***

Its and *it's* are homophones that are often confused.

> *Its* is a possessive pronoun that shows ownership.
>> *We're going to a restaurant that is famous for **its** soup.*
>
> *It's* is a contraction for *it is.*
>> ***It's** going to be a beautiful day.*

Your and *you're* are homophones that are often confused.

> *Your* is a possessive pronoun that shows ownership.
>> *Is that **your** backpack on the ground?*
>
> *You're* is a contraction for *you are.*
>> *Sidney wants to know if **you're** going to call her later.*

Now turn to pages 152–154 to practice identifying pronouns and homophones.

6

Name _____

Pronouns and Homophones 1

Practice

Read each sentence below. Then circle the correct word in parentheses to complete each sentence.

1. If we don't protect the coral reefs, (their, they're) likely to die.

2. If you visit a coral reef, (your, you're) sure to see many wonderful creatures.

3. When you go, remember to bring (your, you're) snorkel.

4. (Its, It's) important to understand that corals are living things.

5. (Their, They're) lives depend on many things being in balance.

6. Because of all the tiny spaces in the Great Barrier Reef, (its, it's) a great place for a fish to hide.

7. (Its, It's) off the coast of Australia.

8. Surely (your, you're) amazed that the Great Barrier is 1,250 miles long.

9. Imagine all the sea life that lives in all (its, it's) cracks and holes.

10. (Your, You're) going to enjoy your visit to the reef.

Name _____

Pronouns and Homophones 2

Practice

Write the homophone that correctly completes each sentence.

1. **their**   **they're**   **there**

    Go to a coral reef and explore the warm, clear waters _____.

2. **Its**   **it's**

    _____ not uncommon to find corals in many bright colors.

3. **their**   **they're**   **there**

    Corals belong to a family of animals, and _____ relatives include jellyfish and anemones.

4. **Its**   **It's**

    _____ even possible to find corals growing on shipwrecks.

5. **its**   **it's**

    A sponge eats by pumping water through holes in _____ body.

Name _____

6. their   they're   there

The bottom of the ocean is a busy place, and many creatures live _____.

7. your   you're

Which one _____ favorite: the sea stars, the sand dollars, or the spiny lobsters?

8. their   they're   there

No matter which one is your favorite, _____ all important to life under the sea.

Lesson E
Adjectives

We use adjectives to tell more about nouns and pronouns. Adjectives help make our language more descriptive by letting us know what a noun or pronoun looks, sounds, smells, tastes, or feels like.

Adjectives

- **Adjectives** are words that describe nouns or pronouns. For example, adjectives may tell what a noun or pronoun looks, sounds, smells, tastes, or feels like. They may also describe something's purpose (for example, *sleeping* bag).

- Adjectives may be placed before a noun or pronoun.

> *She has **red** shoes.*

- Adjectives may be placed after the words *a, an,* and *the.*

> *The bunny has **a fluffy** tail.*

- Adjectives may follow a linking verb.

> *Our teacher **is tall**.*

Now turn to page 156 to practice using adjectives.

Name _____

Adjectives

Practice

Read the sentences below. Write each adjective on the line provided. Some sentences may have more than one adjective.

1. Florida has big mosquitoes. _____

2. Miss Franny wanted a little house with many books. _____

3. That short, smart woman is the librarian. _____

4. She feared that she would seem like a silly woman. _____

5. This book is long and difficult. _____

6. The large bear had a strong smell. _____

7. The bear looked dangerous. _____

8. Winn-Dixie had clean, sharp teeth. _____

9. Miss Franny's father was rich. _____

10. When she saw the dog, she let out a loud, high scream. _____

11. The dog was friendly and clean. _____

12. The bookshelves are high. _____

13. Her father had a loud, scratchy voice. _____

14. The road was not steep at all. _____

15. They cooked the eggs in a frying pan. _____

Order of Adjectives

- **Adjectives** are words that describe nouns or pronouns.

> *Jackie is wearing a **red** dress.*

- You can use more than one **adjective** to describe a noun or pronoun.

> *Jackie is wearing a **long, red** dress.*

- There is an **order of adjectives** that is usually followed when using more than one adjective to describe the same noun or pronoun. The list below shows how the order of adjectives is usually presented, but there are some exceptions and different combinations depending on the situation.

Opinion comes before →	Size/Measure comes before →	Age comes before →	Color comes before →	Origin comes before →	Material comes before →	Purpose
good bad beautiful ugly smart	**size/measure:** big small high low **shape:** round circular square **condition:** broken cracked ripped fresh rotten	new old young	red purple black green dark light	French German American European Italian Korean	iron brass cotton gold wooden vegetable silk linen	sleeping sailing walking

6

• You can use the above list to put adjectives together to describe a noun. When you use more than one adjective to describe a noun or pronoun, you must use commas between the adjectives.

> Barbara bought a **beautiful, new, green, wooden** chair.
>
> Lynn likes the **small, European** sculpture.
>
> The family in the movie lived in a **gorgeous, big, white** house.

Now turn to pages 159–160 to practice using the correct order of adjectives.

Name _____

Order of Adjectives

Practice

Read the following sentences and adjectives. Rewrite the sentences using the adjectives. Be sure to write them in the correct order.

1. Aunt Denise wants a car. (blue, new, European, beautiful)

_____

_____

2. Jacob and Dorothy took a trip. (difficult, long)

_____

3. This is a cake! (chocolate, delicious, huge)

_____

4. I like your purse. (leather, French, brown)

_____

5. The artist got very excited when she saw the paints. (new, exquisite)

_____

_____

6. Look at the boat. (sailing, beautiful, blue)

_____

7. Please pass me the bowl. (serving, small, Japanese)

_____

Name _____

8. He slept in a bag. (sleeping, big, red)

_____

9. The man wore a tie. (old, cotton, dirty)

_____

10. I want to buy the hat. (plastic, big, red)

_____

11. Have you heard the band play? (German, exciting, new)

_____

12. Turn off the lamp. (round, small, reading)

_____

13. I met a snowboarder. (Canadian, talented)

_____

14. Did you taste the sandwich? (delicious, hot, turkey)

_____

15. Dad bought a pan. (silver, frying, used)

_____

Proper and Common Adjectives

- **Proper adjectives** are formed from proper nouns. A proper adjective begins with a capital letter.

> *Chicago summers are hot and humid.*

- Some proper adjectives describe language, races, or nationalities.

> *She has a German accent.*

- Brand names are often proper adjectives.

- **Common adjectives** are not formed from proper nouns. Do not capitalize common adjectives.

> *The chef is wearing a white apron.*

Now turn to pages 162–165 to practice using proper and common adjectives.

6

Name _____

Proper and Common Adjectives 1
Practice

On the line, rewrite each proper adjective correctly.

1. Today I sat and read in the herman w. block room at the library.

_____

_____

2. I understand many spanish words and phrases.

_____

_____

3. Many students at the school are hispanic.

_____

_____

4. I read about a chinese custom of having brides wear red at weddings.

_____

_____

5. The room had a shelf of books about asian countries.

_____

_____

Name _____

6. This library has more books than both pleasantville libraries put together.

_____

_____

7. I won't miss the chill of minnesota winters.

_____

_____

8. I lived near the canadian border, where it got very cold.

_____

_____

Name _____

Proper and Common Adjectives 2

Practice

A. Complete each sentence with an adjective from the box below. Remember to capitalize any proper adjectives.

reddish	atlantic	british	lonely	ohio

1. My dog gets _____ when he's by himself.

2. I gathered shells on the sandy _____ shore.

3. My dog's hair is long and _____.

4. We live in a little _____ town.

5. The librarian's voice sounded _____.

B. Choose the group of words that best completes each sentence. Circle the letter of your choice.

6. I brought home a _____ kitten.

   a. Fluffy, white,

   b. fluffy, white

7. The house was _____.

   a. warm and cozy

   b. warm and Cozy

Common Core State Standards Literacy Handbook

Name _____

8. Her dog is _____.

a. large, brown, and shy

b. large Brown and shy

9. This book contains _____ words.

a. common spanish

b. common Spanish

10. The car had _____ tags.

a. yellow New Jersey

b. yellow New jersey

Articles

- An **article** is a type of adjective. These words are articles: *a, an, the.*

> Look at **the** balloons.

- Use *a* and *an* with singular nouns. Use *a* before most nouns beginning with consonants. Use *an* before words beginning with a vowel or some words beginning with the consonant *h.*

> Do you play **an** instrument?
>
> I took **a** lesson to learn how to play guitar.
>
> His lesson lasts **an** hour.

- Use *the* before singular and plural nouns.

> **The** apples fell from **the** tree.

- An article comes before the noun it describes. Other words sometimes come between the article and the noun it introduces.

> She opened **the** birthday presents.

Now turn to pages 167–168 to practice using articles.

Name _____

Articles 1

Practice

Read each sentence. Put one line under each article. Put two lines under the noun that each article points out.

1. The snake bared his fangs.

2. Father and his family took a different path home.

3. Many villagers went to speak to the elders.

4. They went to see Desert Woman to ask a favor.

5. She placed a noisy rattle on Snake's tail.

6. Rattlesnake continued to threaten the animals.

7. They needed an animal that would make Rattlesnake behave.

8. Desert Woman molded a strange new bird from clay.

9. Roadrunner practiced dancing until he could twirl like a twister.

10. Roadrunner raced down the road to find Rattlesnake.

11. Rattlesnake let out an angry hiss.

12. He struck, but Roadrunner hopped out of the way.

13. Roadrunner danced around Rattlesnake like a whirlwind.

14. Rattlesnake made a promise not to frighten everyone anymore.

15. All the children thanked Roadrunner for helping them.

16. Now the road was safe for everyone to use.

Name _____

Articles 2

Practice

Write the article in each sentence on the line provided.

1. Félipé was a spoiled child. _____

2. He was upset because he had lost the arrow. _____

3. It had landed in a well. _____

4. Ranita had been put under a spell. _____

5. Félipé tried to think of an excuse not to keep his promise. _____

6. He had promised to give Ranita a kiss. _____

7. He was hoping it was all a bad dream. _____

8. She had cast the spell on Ranita. _____

9. Ranita didn't think Félipé would make a good husband. _____

10. Pepé's kiss changed her into a beautiful princess. _____

11. Both Félipé and Ranita refused to get a glass of water for Vieja Sabia. _____

12. The viceroy believed that Félipé should keep the promises he made. _____

13. A viceroy has many things to be concerned about. _____

14. Ranita wore an old hat that belonged to her grandmother. _____

Adjectives that Compare

- Add -er to most adjectives to compare two people, places, or things. This is called the comparative form of an adjective

> My brother is **taller** than I.

- Add -est to most adjectives to compare more than two. This is called the superlative form.

> That is the **longest** movie I have ever seen.

- The comparative form of *good* is *better*. The superlative form of *good* is *best*.

> I thought this book was **better** than the last book I read.
> However, it is not the **best** book I have ever read.

- The comparative form of *bad* is *worse*. The superlative form of *bad* is *worst*.

> The weather is **worse** than it was yesterday.
> Last year we had the **worst** drought in our state's history.

Now turn to pages 170–171 to practice using adjectives that compare.

6

Name _____

Adjectives that Compare 1

Practice

Read each sentence. Underline the adjective in parentheses that correctly completes the sentence.

1. Have you ever imagined exploring the (deeper, deepest) waters of the ocean?

2. The sun looks (brighter, brightest) on the water than it does on land.

3. The Pacific Ocean looks (bluer, bluest) than the Atlantic Ocean.

4. The blue whale is the (larger, largest) mammal of all.

5. The deep water is (colder, coldest) than the shallow water by the shore.

6. This mussel shell is the (prettier, prettiest) shell I found today.

7. I think scuba divers are the (braver, bravest) of all explorers.

8. It is so much (quieter, quietest) under water than it is on the surface.

9. The colors of this fish are the (stranger, strangest) I have ever seen.

10. Andrea is a (faster, fastest) swimmer than Eric.

11. Which of the waves do you think is (higher, highest)?

12. My towel is (sandier, sandiest) than yours.

13. This fish is (smaller, smallest) than the other one.

14. My shell collection is (better, best) than Ralph's.

15. This rock is the (heavier, heaviest) of them.

16. Andrea can stay afloat (longer, longest) than Cyril can.

Name _____

Adjectives that Compare 2

Practice

Rewrite the sentences below, correcting the form or spelling of the underlined adjective.

1. After the sun went down, the air felt chilliest than before.

_____

2. I think fish feel gooder in the ocean than they do in tanks.

_____

3. Dad caught the bigger fish of all.

_____

4. I wonder which ocean is the saltier.

_____

5. The dolphin is one of the smarter animals.

_____

6. The water is calmest than it was yesterday.

_____

7. The winds are badder than they were this morning.

_____

8. That shark has the paler skin I've ever seen.

_____

Comparing with *More* or *Most*

- For long adjectives, use *more* and *most* to compare people, places, or things.

> The brown puppy is **more** playful than the white one.
> The black puppy is the **most** playful puppy.

- Use *more* to compare two people, places, or things.

> This tree has **more** leaves than that one.

- Use *most* to compare more than two.

> California is the **most** beautiful place I have ever seen.

- For some common two-syllable adjectives, such as *happy* and *healthy*, use the ending *-er* or *-est* instead.

> She is **happier** than she was yesterday.
> She is the **happiest** she has ever been.

Now turn to pages 173–175 to practice comparing with *more* or *most*.

Name _____

Comparing with *More* or *Most* 1

Practice

Write *more* or *most* to complete each sentence correctly.

1. Your lemon cake is the _____ delicious dessert of all.

2. Uncle Romie has an even _____ enormous belly than my father.

3. He made the _____ interesting collage I have ever seen.

4. New York City is _____ exciting than my hometown.

5. But for me, North Carolina will always be the _____ comfortable place in the world.

6. Uncle Romie's studio was the _____ glorious mess I had ever seen!

7. I thought my birthday would be _____ pleasant if Aunt Nanette were there.

8. This birthday turned out to be the _____ special birthday ever.

9. Uncle Romie was _____ familiar with New York baseball teams than I was.

10. This summer vacation was _____ enjoyable than last year's vacation.

11. Could this get _____ exciting than yesterday?

12. This is the _____ fun I've ever had.

Name _____

Comparing with *More* or *Most* 2
Practice

Rewrite each sentence. Use the correct form of the adjective.

1. Harlem is the more excitingest place I've ever been.

_____

_____

2. The sounds of the traffic outside made me feel more awaker than at home.

_____

_____

3. At first, Aunt Nanette seemed more caringer than Uncle Romie.

_____

_____

4. My visit to my grandparents' house is the most happier time I can remember.

_____

_____

5. My aunt and uncle are most importanter to me than they used to be.

_____

_____

6. Uncle Romie is the most artisticest person I know.

_____

_____

Name _____

7. I was more carefuller with this collage than I usually am.

_____

_____

8. My mother makes the more excellentest pepper jelly I have ever tasted.

_____

_____

Combining Sentences

- **Adjectives** can be used to combine two sentences into one longer sentence.

> Two Sentences: *He wore a jacket. The jacket was green.*
>
> Combined Sentence: *He wore a green jacket.*

- **Appositives** can be used to combine two sentences into one longer sentence. Appositives are nouns and pronouns that explain or identify the noun they are next to.

> Two Sentences: *My dentist is Dr. Fuller. My dentist went to school with my uncle.*
>
> Combined Sentence: *My dentist, Dr. Fuller, went to school with my uncle.*

- Commas are used to set off many appositives from the rest of the sentence.

> Two Sentences: *Mr. Kullen is running a marathon. Mr. Kullen is our principal.*
>
> Combined Sentence: *Mr. Kullen, our principal, is running a marathon.*

- **Participle phrases** can be used to combine two sentences into one longer sentence.

> *Tracey noticed her cousin.*
> *Tracey's cousin was walking along the shoreline.*
> *Tracey noticed her cousin walking along the shoreline.*

- Use a comma after the participle phrase when it comes at the beginning of the sentence.

> *Removing her coat, Jane ran into the house.*

Now turn to pages 177–178 to practice combining sentences.

Name _____

Combining Sentences 1

Practice

Combine each pair of sentences. Write the new sentence.

1. A coral reef is made up of tiny animals called coral polyps. A coral reef is a home to millions of living things.

   _____

   _____

2. Some coral polyps have skeletons that move back and forth in the water. These skeletons are soft.

   _____

   _____

3. Other coral polyps have skeletons that make up the coral reef. These skeletons are hard.

   _____

   _____

4. All coral polyps catch food with their tentacles. Tentacles are body parts that look like little arms.

   _____

   _____

5. Coral polyps eat plankton. Plankton are tiny plants and animals that float in the water.

   _____

   _____

Name _____

Combining Sentences 2
Practice

Combine each pair of sentences. Write the new sentence on the lines provided.

1. A gray whale has a brain that is the size of a car's engine. Its brain is large.

_____

_____

2. Gray whales communicate with each other. They use low rumbles and other noises.

_____

_____

3. Fluking is when a gray whale raises its tail up in the air and then dives. The tail is wide and flat.

_____

_____

4. A gray whale is breaching. It is leaping out of the water and splashing back in.

_____

_____

5. Gray whales swim south in the fall. They are headed to warmer water.

_____

_____

Comparing with *Good* and *Bad*

- The adjective *good* becomes *better* or *best* when it is used to compare.

> The grocery store sells **good** sandwiches.
> Bob's Deli sells **better** sandwiches.
> My mom makes the **best** sandwich.

- Use *better* to compare two people, places, or things.

> I think a cat is a **better** pet than a bird.

- Use *best* to compare more than two.

> That band plays the **best** music.

- The adjective *bad* becomes *worse* or *worst* when it is used to compare.

> The salad tastes **bad.**
> The soup tastes **worse** than the salad tastes.
> This is the **worst** meal.

- Use *worse* to compare two people, places, or things.

> My drawing is **worse** than my painting.

- Use *worst* to compare more than two.

> We have the **worst** seats in the theater.

Now turn to pages 180–181 to practice comparing with *good* and *bad*.

Name _____

Comparing with *Good* and *Bad* 1

Practice

Write *better* or *best* to complete each sentence.

1. The Black Hills Wild Horse Sanctuary is one of the _____ places to see wild horses.

2. My friend thinks horses are _____ companions than dogs.

3. Dayton Hyde thinks that running free is _____ for horses than being stuck in one place.

4. He thought the _____ choice would be to fence the horses in at first.

5. Because he grew up on a ranch, Dayton is a much _____ rider than most of us.

6. Life was _____ for most wild horses in the 1800s than it was in the 1900s.

7. Conditions were _____ for population growth after a 1971 law outlawed the capture of wild horses.

8. Dayton Hyde created the _____ place for wild horses to run free.

9. Horse ranches are the _____ places to learn to ride.

10. His horse is _____ at racing than mine is.

11. This is the _____ spot for a horse to drink.

12. Is it _____ to ride side saddle or western style?

Name _____

Comparing with *Good* and *Bad* 2

Practice

Write *worse* or *worst* to complete each sentence correctly.

1. The invention of barbed-wire fences made life _____ for wild horses than before.

2. During the _____ period, the population of horses fell below 17,000.

3. Hunger and thirst were the _____ threats to horses.

4. Seeing wild horses in fenced feedlots made Dayton Hyde feel _____ than he had for a long time.

5. The ranch was no _____ than the feedlot.

6. The thought of the horses breaking down the fence was Dayton's

   _____ fear.

7. Conditions were _____ for horses after more land was settled.

8. The cold felt _____ for the cowboys than it did for the horses.

9. This is the _____ time to ride a horse.

10. My saddle sore is no _____ than yours, I suppose.

11. That's not the _____ riding I've ever seen.

12. That trail is much _____ than this trail.

Lesson F
Adverbs

We use adverbs to tell more about verbs. Adverbs help us describe how, when, where, or why an action takes place. We also use adverbs to compare people, places, and things.

Adverbs

- An **adverb** tells more about the verb.

> *Anita **quickly** walked home.*

- Some **adverbs** tell *how* an action takes place.

> *We **quietly** snuck downstairs.*

- Some *adverbs* tell *when* an action takes place. These adverbs may describe how often an action takes place.

> *Marcus talks to his grandmother **daily.***

- Some **adverbs** tell *where* an action takes place.

> *I will not walk **there.***

Now turn to pages 183–184 to practice using adverbs.

Name _____

Adverbs 1

Practice

Read each sentence and underline the adverb.

1. In 1848, many people quickly moved to California in search of gold.

2. The forty-niners desperately hoped to find gold.

3. I recently read an interesting story about the California Gold Rush.

4. Show your father the treasure map that you found yesterday.

5. The miner dug deeply into the hole to see if there was gold inside.

6. I finally found something in the river that I think is gold.

7. On our field trip to the gold mine, our guide cautiously led us through a dark tunnel.

8. Matt and Eric were mysteriously standing by a muddy road.

9. Raven always wanted to travel back in time to see how her neighborhood used to look.

10. They eagerly waited to join the wagon train to California.

Name _____

Adverbs 2

Practice

Underline the adverb in each sentence. Then write if the adverb tells *how*, *when*, or *where* the action takes place.

1. My mother and I went to the library together for information about our ancestors.

   _____

2. Tomorrow we will visit our local museum of natural history. _____

3. Were they traveling far in search of gold? _____

4. Did James Marshall first find gold at Sutter's Mill? _____

5. John Sutter, Jr., built a new city nearby. _____

6. We patiently sifted the sand for gold. _____

7. Our uncle examined the rock thoroughly. _____

8. He carelessly threw the stone back in the water. _____

9. That greedy miner looked at them suspiciously. _____

10. We then found the gold. _____

Common Core State Standards Literacy Handbook

Using *Good* and *Well*

- *Good* is an adjective and is used to describe nouns.

> That was a **good** movie.

- *Well* is an adverb that tells *how* about a verb.

> The actress sang **well.**

- Do not confuse the adjective *good* with the adverb *well.*

> Our school has a **good** basketball team.
> Our school's basketball team played **well.**

- Use *well* as an adjective when you refer to someone's health.

> Victor wasn't feeling **well,** so he went to the nurse's office.

Now turn to page 186 to practice using *good* and *well.*

Name _____

Using *Good* and *Well*

Practice

Complete each sentence by writing the word *good* or *well* on the line.

1. Today our team did _____ in the class treasure-hunt game.

2. Our teacher hid the treasure pieces so _____ that they were very hard to find.

3. It was a _____ experience to win the game for a second year.

4. The other team also did _____, but we found the pieces faster than they did.

5. Though I didn't feel _____, I helped find the last hidden treasure piece.

6. This river is a _____ place to look for gold pieces.

7. Grandfather, would it be a _____ idea to look for gold in the river?

8. If we pan for gold all day and night, we should _____.

9. We can have a _____ time swimming in the water if we do not find anything.

10. Is your father feeling _____ enough to come with us?

Comparing with Adverbs

- An **adverb** can compare two or more actions.

> *I think my sister can run **faster** than I.*

- Add -*er* to short adverbs to compare two actions.

> *Lee jumped **higher** than Anna did.*

- Add -*est* to short adverbs to compare more than two actions.

> *Sarah talked the **loudest** of us all.*

- Use *more* or *most* to compare adverbs that are long or that end in -*ly*.

> *Our fans cheered **more** enthusiastically than the other team's fans.*
> *She practices the **most** frequently of all of her friends.*

- Use *more* to compare two actions and *most* to compare more than two actions.

> *I talk **more** than my brother does.*
> *My father talks the **most** out of all of our family members.*

- To make comparisons using the adverb *well*, use *better* and *best*.

> *Sasha dances **well**.*
> *Jorge dances **better** than Sasha dances.*
> *Margaret dances the **best**.*

Now turn to pages 188–189 to practice comparing with adverbs.

Name _____

Comparing with Adverbs 1
Practice

A. Add *-er* or *-est* to each boldfaced adverb to complete the sentences below.

1. fast   My brother runs _____ than I do.

2. close   The spaceship traveled _____ to Mars than Venus.

3. hard   I think she works _____ of all the students in the class.

B. Complete each sentence using more or most.

4. Do you use the computer _____ often at home or at school?

5. Which swimmer started _____ quickly of all?

6. Does Craig or Ana write _____ neatly?

7. Captain Smith sailed the _____ skillfully of all.

Name _____

Comparing with Adverbs 2
Practice

A. Use *more* or *most* with the underlined adverb in each first sentence to complete the two sentences that follow.

1. The train that Chester was on shook harshly as it moved on the track.

   The second train shook _____ every now and then.

   But the subway car shook _____ of all.

2. Harry Cat speedily jumped toward Chester and Tucker Mouse.

   Chester jumped the _____ of all into the matchbox.

   Chester jumped _____ than Harry Cat.

B. Use *better* or *best* or *worse* or *worst* to replace the underlined adverb in the two sentences that follow.

3. Chester chirps well when he is excited.

   Chester chirps _____ when he is scared than when he is tired.

   But Chester chirps _____ of all when he is happy.

4. He sings badly when it is very hot.

   He sings _____ when he is sick than when he is healthy.

   He sings _____ of all when he has a cold.

Correcting Double Negatives

- A **negative** is a statement that means "no." Most statements can be changed to a negative form.

> I like chess.
>
> I **do not** like chess.

- Many verbs with *not* can be made into contractions.

> We **did not** go to the zoo.
>
> We **didn't** go to the zoo.

- Do not use two negatives in the same sentence. You can fix a sentence with two negatives by removing one.

> Incorrect: Marc **didn't** worry **nothing** about his math test.
>
> Correct: Marc **didn't** worry about his math test.

- You can correct a sentence with two negatives by changing one negative to a positive word.

> Incorrect: I **didn't** know **nothing** about sharks until I did my research.
>
> Correct: I **didn't** know **anything** about sharks until I did my research.

Now turn to pages 191–192 to practice correcting double negatives.

Name _____

Correcting Double Negatives 1
Practice

Rewrite each sentence by changing it to a negative form.

1. Hakeem wants to study science.

_____

2. He likes to be near dirt and bones.

_____

3. His teacher thought he would pass her class.

_____

4. He is happy when science class begins.

_____

5. Hakeem had seen a piece of amber.

_____

6. His opinion of science has changed.

_____

7. Hakeem does get bored in class now.

_____

8. There is a better way to thank his teacher for what she did.

_____

_____

Name _____

Correcting Double Negatives 2

Practice

Rewrite each sentence below by dropping a negative or changing one negative to a positive word.

1. I haven't found nothing in this area yet.

_____

2. Our team didn't waste no time finding the skeleton.

_____

3. Don't never go out in the bright sun without putting on a hat.

_____

4. There isn't no place to find dinosaur bones here.

_____

5. I wouldn't never want to see a dinosaur in real life.

_____

6. I don't not know where the oldest fossil was found.

_____

7. The team couldn't find the sunken ship nowhere.

_____

8. Iris didn't put no labels on the stones she found.

_____

Common Core State Standards Literacy Handbook

Relative Adverbs

- An **adverb** tells more about a verb. It can tell *how*, *when*, *where*, or *why* an action takes place.

> She **quickly** ran to the store.

- A **relative adverb** introduces a group of words, or a clause, that tells more about a noun. Relative adverbs can be used instead of a relative pronoun plus a preposition. There are three main **relative adverbs**: *where*, *when*, and *why*.

> This is the store **in which** I bought my backpack.
> (relative pronoun plus preposition)
> This is the store **where** I bought my backpack.
> (relative adverb)

- The relative adverb *where* means "in which" or "at which" and is used to refer to a place.

> This is the place **where** we met.

- The relative adverb *when* means "in which" or "at which" and is used to refer to a time expression.

> Friday is the day **when** we met him.

- The relative adverb *why* means "for which" and is used to refer to a reason.

> I don't know the reason **why** Larry isn't in class today.

Now turn to page 194 to practice using relative adverbs.

Name _____

Relative Adverbs

Practice

Read the sentences below. Fill in the blanks with the correct relative adverb.

1. I do not know the place _____ she works.

2. Reese didn't know the reason _____ her sister was mad.

3. Do you remember the time _____ we found the hidden waterfall?

4. This is the hospital _____ Jack was born.

5. Do you know the reason _____ so many people visit this place?

6. This is the town _____ Josh grew up.

7. The day _____ I arrived was very nice.

8. That farm is _____ Aunt Denise bought the fresh corn.

9. The scary movie was the reason _____ I couldn't sleep.

10. This is the store _____ I bought my jacket.

11. The reason _____ I didn't finish my homework is because I was sick.

12. I can't remember the time _____ we first met.

Lesson G
Prepositions and Conjunctions

When we speak and write, we use prepositions to relate a noun or pronoun to another word in a sentence. We use conjunctions to join parts of a sentence. Prepositions and conjunctions are important parts of grammar.

Prepositions

- A **preposition** comes before a noun or pronoun and relates that noun or pronoun to another word in a sentence.

> Marissa walked **under** the bridge.

- Common prepositions are *about, above, across, after, around, at, before, behind, by, down, during, for, from, in, into, near, of, on, over, to, under,* and *with*.

> John fell **down** the stairs.
> Ryan stepped **over** the spilled milk.

Now turn to pages 196–197 to practice using prepositions.

6

Name _____

Prepositions 1
Practice

Complete each sentence by adding a preposition.

1. Papa brought home a little flying machine _____ the kids.

2. Mama never complained _____ Orv and Will's messes.

3. The two older brothers did not agree _____ Orv and Will's activities.

4. Only the family knew _____ Orv and Will's plans.

5. There was no place _____ their home where they could fly a plane.

6. Flying _____ Kitty Hawk grounds was a good idea.

7. Orv and Will's plane flew _____ the ground.

8. Katherine took her first ride almost six years _____ the first flight.

9. Riding _____ an early plane was dangerous.

10. I like the wind blowing _____ my hair.

11. The plane landed _____ the field.

12. He left the plans _____ the floor.

Name _____

Prepositions 2
Practice

Complete each sentence below by writing the missing preposition.

1. Papa tossed the flying machine _____ the air.

2. Reuchlin and Lorin looked down _____ Orv and Will's new hobby.

3. Will sold kites to the other kids _____ school.

4. Orv and Will built their first craft _____ the bicycle shop.

5. However, the Flyer was so big, they had to build it _____ the shop.

6. They tacked their plans _____ the wall.

7. He hopped _____ the plane's body.

Prepositional Phrases

- A **prepositional phrase** is a group of words that begins with a **preposition** and ends with a noun or pronoun.

  *Molly hid **behind the curtain.***

- When a pronoun follows a preposition, it should be an object pronoun, such as *me, you, him, her, it, us,* or *them.*

  *My sister and I went **with them** to the park.*

Now turn to pages 199–200 to practice using prepositional phrases.

Name _____

Prepositional Phrases 1

Practice

A. Underline the prepositional phrases in the following sentences.

1. When they finished their first plane, Orv and Katherine went on a camping trip.

2. Will flew the plane over a group of boys.

3. Katherine helped her brothers by managing their shop.

4. In their letters, they told her everything they were doing.

5. Will said that Kitty Hawk was a safe place for practice.

6. The world had never before seen a craft fly in the air.

7. First, they controlled their aircraft from the ground.

8. They came home to Dayton with a new idea.

9. Orv and Will worked from day to night.

10. They had their friend Charlie build an engine for their new aircraft.

B. Write an object pronoun on the line to complete each sentence.

11. Orv and Will thanked their sister and spoke highly about _____ to reporters.

12. The ground seemed very far away when they flew above _____.

Name _____

Prepositional Phrases 2

Practice

Underline the prepositional phrase in each of the sentences below.

1. Orv and Will took weeks preparing for their first flight.

2. On December 14, 1903, the *Flyer* rattled down the track.

3. Will flew the aircraft fifteen feet above ground.

4. Orv watched the flight from the ground.

5. One day, human beings would fly around the world.

6. They kept the plans in a safe place.

7. The crowd stood in place.

8. The plane stayed above the ground.

Coordinating Conjunctions

- A **coordinating conjunction** joins parts of a sentence that are grammatically equal or similar. A coordinating conjunction shows that the parts it joins are similar in importance and structure.

> *I like orange juice **and** apple juice.*
> *Ruth likes orange juice, **but** Edward likes apple juice.*

- Coordinating conjunctions always come between the words or clauses that they join.

> *Should we go to the park **or** the pool?*

- A coordinating conjunction can join a word to a word.

> *Many people like cookies **and** milk.*

- A coordinating conjunction can join a phrase to a phrase.

> *The gold is hidden at the beach **or** by the lake.*

- A coordinating conjunction can join a clause to a clause.

> *What you say **and** what you do are two different things.*

- A coordinating conjunction can join three or more words, phrases, or clauses to create a series. When this happens, use commas between the elements.

> *We ate salad, chicken, and apple sauce for dinner.*

- When a coordinating conjunction joins independent clauses, place a comma before the conjunction.

> *I want to teach math in the future, **so** I am working hard in math class now.*

- There are seven coordinating conjunctions. They are: *and, or, for, nor, but, yet,* and *so.*

Now turn to page 203 to practice using coordinating conjunctions.

Name _____

Coordinating Conjunctions

Practice

Complete each sentence by writing a coordinating conjunction on the line provided.

1. Jessica _____ Billy are married.

2. Should we go get frozen yogurt _____ lemonade?

3. Kristen wants to take Spanish lessons, _____ she can learn how to speak the language.

4. I love to travel, _____ I don't like traveling by bus.

5. John was mad at Julie, _____ he went for a walk.

6. I live in the city, _____ my cousins live in the country.

7. Is this seat taken, _____ may I sit here?

8. It's raining outside, _____ I brought my umbrella.

9. Liz likes to go skiing _____ swimming.

10. The tour bus stopped at the art museum _____ the planetarium.

Subordinating Conjunctions

- A **subordinate (or dependent) clause** is a group of words that *cannot* stand alone. It depends on the rest of the sentence for its meaning.

> *After we ate dinner*

- A **main clause** is a group of words that *can* stand alone.

> We paid the check.

- A **subordinating conjunction** joins a dependent clause with a main clause.

> *After we ate dinner, we paid the check.*

- Some subordinating conjunctions include: *after, although, as long as, before, because if, since, unless, until, wherever, while, once.*

> **Unless** *we go now, we'll miss the bus.*
> **Because** *he loved music, he continued to take piano lessons.*
> *She walked up on stage* **as though** *she had been an actress all her life.*

Now turn to page 205 to practice using subordinating conjunctions.

Name _____

Subordinating Conjunctions

Practice

Read the sentences below. Then circle the subordinating conjunction in each sentence.

1. Sally cleaned her room while she was talking on the phone.

2. After the rain stopped, the dog ran into the mud to play.

3. Because we are late, we missed the movie.

4. My mom won't let me play outside until I finish my homework.

5. Even though I like you, I don't want to go to the movie with you.

6. Whenever we go on vacation, my brother and I have to share a suitcase.

7. Once you get to Main Street, you will turn left.

8. Tina doesn't want to go to the party because she doesn't feel well.

9. You're not allowed to have dessert unless you finish your dinner.

10. Although I like pineapples, I don't like pineapple juice.

Lesson H
Capitalization

Capitalization is an important part of writing. Capitalization helps readers and speakers know when a new sentence has started, when the name of a person or place is being referred to, what the title of a book is, and much more.

Capitalization

- Every sentence begins with a capital letter. Remember, a sentence can be a statement, a question, a command, or an exclamation.

> *Jackie went swimming.*
>
> *Do not run near the pool.*
>
> *Do you like to swim?*
>
> *I love to swim!*

- A **proper noun** names a particular person, place, or thing. Some proper nouns contain more than one word. Each important word begins with a capital letter.

> *Examples: Thomas Jefferson, Crater Lake, National Baseball Hall of Fame*

- The pronoun *I* must always be capitalized.

> *I don't know about you, but I really enjoy reading books.*

- The name of a **day**, **month**, or **holiday** begins with a capital letter.

> *She was born on a Monday.*
>
> *My favorite month is October.*
>
> *I got a card for Valentine's Day.*

- Capitalize proper nouns that name **historical events** or **documents**, **languages**, **races**, or **nationalities.**

> *We learned about the Revolutionary War in class.*
>
> *Do you know who signed the Declaration of Independence?*
>
> *My grandfather speaks German and French.*
>
> *My grandmother is Asian.*

- Capitalize the first and last words and all important words in the **titles of books and newspapers.** Also, underline the titles of books, magazines, and newspapers.

> *I finished reading* The Kapok Tree *last night.*
>
> *My sister reads our local newspaper,* The Chicago Tribune.

- Capitalize **proper adjectives**.

> *Our teacher has a French accent.*

Now turn to pages 208–214 to practice correct capitalization.

6

Name _____

Capitalization 1

Practice

Rewrite each sentence correctly by putting capital letters where they belong. Remember to underline the titles.

1. tom's class started reading a new book today.

_____

_____

2. Tom wanted to read a book called hatchet, but his teacher chose a different book for them to read.

_____

_____

3. Molly asked tom if he was upset about not getting to read Hatchet.

_____

_____

4. tom said he wasn't upset, but he read an interesting article about the book's author in the aspen Daily newspaper.

_____

_____

5. Molly asked Tom if he remembered who wrote hatchet.

_____

_____

Name _____

6. Tom told molly that Gary paulsen wrote the Book.

_____

_____

7. Molly suggested they read hatchet on their own.

_____

_____

8. Tom thought that was a great idea. Maybe they could even write an article for their school's newspaper, The weekly Lion.

_____

_____

Name _____

Capitalization 2
Practice

Rewrite each sentence below correctly.

1. I like to play baseball with my brother matt and his friends.

_____

_____

2. Last saturday, we played all afternoon.

_____

_____

3. I am also part of the dallas little league.

_____

_____

4. My cousin Karen is the best pitcher I know.

_____

_____

5. We play ball together when i visit her in florida.

_____

_____

Name _____

6. I haven't seen her since thanksgiving.

_____

_____

7. She has a rare baseball card for mickey mantle.

_____

_____

8. My uncle listens to games on a radio station that broadcasts in spanish.

_____

_____

Name _____

Capitalization 3

Practice

Rewrite the invitation below. Fix any spelling, punctuation, and grammar mistakes. Remember to capitalize each important word in a proper noun.

westfield little league invites you to attend

our 2009 most valuable player awards ceremony

at five o'clock on sunday, january 25

westfield town hall

501 central avenue, westfield, Virginia

Please contact sally and jim smith at 555-1212 if you plan to attend.

We hope you will join us!

_____

_____

_____

_____

_____

_____

_____

Common Core State Standards Literacy Handbook

Name _____

Capitalization 4

Practice

Rewrite each sentence, making sure the titles are written correctly.

1. One of Ben Franklin's best-known books is titled poor Richard's almanac.

_____

_____

2. Lewis Latimer wrote a book called incandescent electric lighting in 1890.

_____

_____

3. I learned about Thomas Edison and Lewis Latimer from an article I read in the magazine science for kids.

_____

_____

4. Someday I would like to get a story published in my local newspaper, the miami herald.

_____

_____

Name _____

Capitalization 5

Practice

Complete each sentence with an adjective from the box below. Remember to capitalize any proper adjectives.

| reddish | atlantic | british | lonely | ohio |

1. My dog gets _____ when he's by himself.

2. I gathered shells on the sandy _____ shore.

3. My dog's hair is long and _____.

4. We live in a little _____ town.

5. The librarian's voice sounded _____.

Lesson I
Punctuation

Punctuation helps readers and speakers know when to pause, when a question is being asked, when a sentence has ended, and much more. There are different types of punctuation that are used at different times.

End Punctuation

- All sentences begin with a capital letter and end with a period, a question mark, or an exclamation point.

> *I have brown hair.*
> *What color hair do you have?*
> *Look at all of those people!*

- A **statement** is a sentence that tells something. It ends with a period. (.)

> *Sarah went sailing yesterday.*

- A **question** is a sentence that asks something and ends with a question mark. (?)

> *What are your hobbies?*

- A **command** tells or asks someone to do something. It ends with a period. (.)

> *Call me when you get home.*

- An **exclamation** shows strong feeling. It ends with an exclamation point. (!)

> *Riding a horse is fun!*

Now turn to pages 216–217 to practice using end punctuation.

Name _____

End Punctuation 1

Practice

Decide if each sentence is a *statement*, a *question*, a *command*, or an *exclamation*. Write the type of sentence on the line.

1. His favorite sandwich is salami.

_____

2. Can you lend me a dollar?

_____

3. Don't forget your lunch.

_____

4. The kittens are hiding.

_____

5. What a funny story!

_____

6. That stain looks like mustard.

_____

Name _____

End Punctuation 2

Practice

Write each sentence with the correct punctuation.

1. I thought Jack took my lunch

_____

2. Did you ever make a mistake like that

_____

3. Cats are my favorite pets

_____

4. I don't have any money

_____

5. Wow, I can't believe the cat ate my lunch

_____

6. Bring the kittens to my office

_____

Commas

- A **comma** tells the reader to pause between the words that it separates.

- Use commas to separate three or more words in a series.

> *We enjoyed the mountains, the trees, and the clouds in the park.*

- Do not use a comma after the last word in a series.

> *We saw bears, lions, and penguins at the zoo.*

- Use a comma before *and*, *but*, or *or* when you join two sentences to form a compound sentence.

> *Dan went to the beach.*
> *I had to stay home and do homework.*
> *Dan went to the beach, but I had to stay home and do homework.*

- Do not use a comma before *and* when you combine two subjects or two predicates.

> *Lola ate a burrito.*
> *Lola drank a glass of juice.*
> *Lola ate a burrito and drank a glass of juice.*

Now turn to pages 219–222 to practice using commas.

Name _____

Commas 1

Practice

Rewrite the sentences below by adding commas where they belong.

1. He fed milked and groomed the cows.

_____

2. Go to the store and get flour eggs and sugar.

_____

3. Mexico Ireland and China are three countries I have visited.

_____

4. Bring wood nails and a hammer.

_____

5. We have mules horses and pigs on our ranch.

_____

6. This city feels dirty strange and lonely.

_____

7. Mosquitoes spiders and ants annoyed us.

_____

Name _____

8. I brought my diary my pencil and an eraser.

_____

9. My mother father and brother are coming along.

_____

10. I miss the house my dog and our friends.

_____

Name _____

Commas 2

Practice

Use *and*, *or*, or *but* to combine two sentences into a compound sentence. Or, use *and* or *or* to combine subjects or predicates.

1. My family loves camping. I prefer reading indoors.

_____

_____

2. A volcano steams. A volcano erupts.

_____

_____

3. Mom likes to hike. I come with her.

_____

_____

4. A moose might walk by. A wolf might walk by.

_____

_____

5. Fire burned some of the park. Other parts were untouched.

_____

_____

6. Karen went hiking. I'm going with her next time.

_____

_____

Name _____

7. The Lower Falls are well known. Others don't even have a name.

_____

_____

8. Serena is camping. Maria is camping.

_____

_____

Quotation Marks

- Use **quotation marks** at the beginning and end of a speaker's exact words or a quotation from a text.

> *"I don't want to go swimming today," Mike said.*
> *The guidebook says, "Be prepared to stand in line."*

- Commas and periods always go inside quotation marks.

> *Jason said, "Please come to the lake with me."*
> *"Plant early this spring," the almanac advises.*

- Do not use quotation marks when you do not use the speaker's exact words.

> *Kelly told me she is nervous about her book report.*
> *The encyclopedia says that many languages are spoken in Canada.*

- Use a comma before the opening quotation mark if the sentence begins before the quote.

> *Mr. Franklin walked in the room and said, "I have something to tell you."*
> *The flyer said, "Bring a friend!"*

6

- Use a comma before the closing quotation mark if a sentence continues after the quote.

> *The police officer said, "Thank you for your help," and then walked away.*
> *Dr. Chen states, "The key to preventing diabetes is good nutrition," but that is not the whole story.*

- Use quotation marks before and after the titles of short works.

> *I wrote a story called "Jasmine's Travels."*

Now turn to pages 225–228 to practice using quotation marks.

Name _____

Quotation Marks 1

Practice

Rewrite each sentence correctly by putting capital letters and quotation marks where they belong.

1. Roberto asked me, have you ever seen a rattlesnake?

_____

_____

2. no, I never have, I answered.

_____

_____

3. Roberto told me that rattlesnakes are his favorite animal.

_____

_____

4. On the board, our science teacher wrote, rattlesnakes are related to lizards.

_____

_____

5. As you will read in your science books, both rattlesnakes and lizards are reptiles, she said.

_____

_____

6. some reptiles can even change colors, Andrea said.

_____

_____

Name _____

7. yes, you are thinking of chameleons, Andrea, replied Ms. Giordello.

_____

_____

8. why do they do that? asked Hakim.

_____

_____

Name _____

Quotation Marks 2

Practice

Rewrite each sentence correctly by adding commas and quotation marks where they belong.

1. Our class just finished reading a great story, The Lion and the Queen.

_____

_____

2. The very last line of the story said, the lion and the queen lived happily ever after.

_____

_____

3. Mr. Peterson asked, Did you like the story?

_____

_____

4. We liked it very much the students said.

_____

_____

5. Then let's put on a play about it, the teacher said.

_____

_____

Name _____

6. Mr. Peterson looked around and said James, you can play the lion.

_____

_____

7. That's great! I'm really excited, said James with a grin.

_____

_____

8. Grace raised her hand and asked Can I play the queen?

_____

_____

9. Mr. Peterson said Sure, as long as the rest of the class doesn't mind.

_____

_____

10. Once upon a time, is how the story begins.

_____

_____

Apostrophes

- An **apostrophe** takes the place of letters left out of a contraction.

> do not—don't   could not—couldn't   they are—they're

- Possessive pronouns do not have apostrophes.

> My aunt and uncle drove up in their car.

- Be careful not to confuse possessive nouns with contractions.

> They're not going on vacation.
> We're having dinner at their house.

Now turn to pages 230–231 to practice using apostrophes.

Name _____

Apostrophes 1

Practice

Read the pairs of sentences below. Then write the correct form of the underlined incorrect contraction or possessive pronoun on the line.

1. Have you heard about underwater parks? <u>Their</u> places where sea life is protected.

   _____

2. Fish and people both have homes. The ocean is <u>there's</u>, and the land is ours.

   _____

3. Clean water is important for sea life. <u>Its</u> like clean air for us.

   _____

4. A lobster's skeleton is on the outside of <u>it's</u> body. Where's <u>you're</u> skeleton?

   _____

5. Do you want to see the reef? <u>Your</u> going to need a snorkel.

   _____

Common Core State Standards Literacy Handbook

Name _____

Apostrophes 2

Practice

Read each sentence below. Then decide if the underlined word in each sentence is a *possessive noun* or a *contraction*. Write your answer on the line provided.

1. The <u>world's</u> oceans are home to thousands of miles of coral reefs.

   _____

2. The <u>world's</u> filled with wonders.

   _____

3. Some people think that <u>coral's</u> a plant, but really it's an animal.

   _____

4. <u>Coral's</u> relatives have soft, jelly-like bodies.

   _____

5. The hawksbill turtle is one of the <u>reef's</u> many visitors.

   _____

Standard
2.d

Lesson J
Spelling

Knowing how to spell words is an important skill to have. Sometimes spelling words can be difficult. There are strategies and tools you can use to help make spelling words easier. In this lesson, you will learn how to improve your spelling.

Tips for Improving Spelling

Use these strategies to help you become a better speller.

- **Homophones** Learn common homophones and make sure you have used the correct homophone in your writing.

> *They're going to **their** house. They live over **there**.*

- **Rhyming Words** Think of a word you know that has the same spelling pattern as the word you want to spell, such as a rhyming word.

> *stew   blew   knew*

- **Use words that you know** how to spell to help you spell new words.

> *blow + sock = block*

- **Make up clues** to help you remember the spelling.

> ***u** and **i** build a house; a **pi**ece of **pi**e; the princi**pal** is your **pal***

- **Related Words** Think of a related word to help you spell a word with a silent letter or a hard-to-hear sound.

> *sign—signal   relative—related*

- **Syllables** Divide the word into syllables.

> *par a chute*

- **Prefixes and Suffixes** Learn to spell prefixes and suffixes you often use in writing.

- **Word Chunks** Look for word chunks or smaller words that help you remember the spelling of the word.

> *hippopotamus = hippo pot am us*

- **Change the way you say the word** to yourself to help with the spelling.

> *knife = /k nīf /; beauty = /bē ū tē/*

- **Visualizing** Think of the times you may have seen the word in reading, on signs, or in a textbook. Try to remember how it looked. Write the word in different ways. Which one looks correct?

> ~~*atick*~~   ~~*atik*~~   *attic*

- **Dictionary** Become familiar with a dictionary and use it often.

- **Personal Word List** Keep an alphabetical Personal Word List in your word study notebook. Write words you often have trouble spelling.

Now turn to pages 234–235 to practice using tips for improving spelling.

Name _____

Tips for Improving Spelling

Practice

Homophones:

Circle the correct homophones in the sentences below.

    1. I bought (to, two) apples. Linda bought (two, too) apples (too, to).

Rhyming Words:

Write three words that rhyme with *fall*.

    1. _____   **2.** _____   **3.** _____

Using Words That You Know:

Write two or more words that you know. Then try to spell a new word based on those two words.

_____   _____   _____

Making up Clues:

Write a clue to help you remember the spelling of the word *together*.

_____

Related Words:

Think of a related word to help you spell the word *sea*.

_____

Syllables:

Divide the following word into syllables to help you remember how to spell it: *document*.

_____

Name _____

Prefixes and Suffixes:

Write three words that end in suffix -*ly*.

1. _____ 2. _____ 3. _____

Changing the Way You Say a Word:

Think of a different way to say the word *people*. Then write on the line below how you would say it.

_____

Visualizing:

Think of a word you have seen while reading. Then try to remember how it looked. On the line below, write the word in different ways and ask yourself which spelling looks correct.

_____

Using the Dictionary:

Think of word you have seen while reading. Then use one of the strategies you learned about to try to spell it. Write the word on the line below. Then look up the spelling in the dictionary to see whether you spelled it correctly.

_____

Using Resources to Check Spelling

- One way to check the spelling of unfamiliar or difficult words is in school. You can use the resources your teacher has made available. For instance, you might look at a **word wall,** which is usually a large chart that has vocabulary words or other difficult words listed on it. You might also look at **posters, charts,** and **pictures** that are displayed in your classroom.

- You can also use a **dictionary** to look up misspelled words or words that are difficult to spell. To look up a word in the dictionary, you need to know what letter or letters the word starts with. You can use the spelling strategies you learned about to help you start to spell the word. For instance, you can practice visualizing the word or dividing the word into syllables. Once you have the beginning of the word sounded out, use the dictionary to check the spelling.

- When you type on the computer you might notice that the spelling of a certain word automatically changes or that a word appears to be underlined. This feature is called spell check. Spell check might sound like a good way to check your spelling, but it is not a reliable resource. Often the spell check does not know the correct word you're trying to write. For instance, think about the homographs *too* and *to*. If you meant to write *too,* the computer might change the word to *to,* which would be incorrect.

- Another resource you can use to check the spelling of words is a word list. To create a word list, write down words you find difficult to spell. You might use a notebook or a set of note cards to create this resource. You can organize your words by alphabet or by a spelling rule.

Now turn to page 237 to practice using resources to check spelling.

Name _____

Using Resources to Check Spelling

Practice

On the lines below write any words that you have trouble spelling. You can look up the spelling in a dictionary or write them when you see them spelled correctly. Continue to add words to this list and use it as a reference when you're writing.

_____

_____

_____

_____

_____

_____

_____

_____

_____

_____

_____

_____

_____

_____

_____

_____

_____

Spelling Commonly Confused Words Correctly

- The English language includes some confusing words that are often misused. The following charts will help you understand how to use these words properly.

Words	Correct Usage
bad	*Bad* is an adjective. It means "the opposite of good." *He is a **bad** tennis player.*
badly	*Badly* is an adverb. It means "in a bad manner." *The girl behaved **badly** at the concert.*
can	*Can* means "to be able or capable of doing something." *Jeffery **can** play the clarinet.*
may	*May* expresses or asks permission. *You **may** go to the movies on Friday.*
good	*Good* is an adjective that describes something positive. *I read a **good** book last night.*
well	*Well* is usually an adverb. It gives more information about the verb by telling "how." *The author writes **well**.*
its	*Its* is a possessive pronoun. *Its* has no apostrophe. *Did the dog find **its** bone?*
it's	*It's* is the contraction for "it is." The apostrophe takes the place of the *i* in *is*. ***It's** time for us to leave.*
lay	*Lay* means "to put something down." ***Lay** the towels on the shelf.*
lie	*Lie* means "to recline or rest." *My grandmother **lies** down every afternoon.*
learn	*Learn* means "to get knowledge." *The children **learn** about dinosaurs at the museum.*
teach	*Teach* means "to give knowledge." *The veterinarians **teach** us how to take care of our pets.*

- Some words are easily confused because they sound the same.

Words	Correct Usage
set	*Set* means "to put something down or in a certain place." *He* **set** *the books on his desk.*
sit	*Sit* means "to be seated." *Please* **sit** *in the living room.*
their	*Their* is a possessive pronoun meaning "belonging to them." *My neighbors have a tree house in* **their** *yard.*
they're	*They're* is a contraction meaning "they are." **They're** *planning a birthday party for Miguel.*
to	*To* is a direction word meaning "toward." *We walk* **to** *school together.*
too	*Too* means "also" or "very." *I will eat ice cream,* **too.** *This math problem is* **too** *hard.*
whose	*Whose* is an adjective showing possession. *Ted knows* **whose** *pencil that is.*
who's	*Who's* is the contraction for "who is." The apostrophe takes the place of the *i* in *is.* **Who's** *going skating next weekend?*
your	*Your* is a possessive pronoun that means "something belongs to you." *This is* **your** *game.*
you're	*You're* is the contraction for "you are." **You're** *going to love my new joke.*

6

- Some words are easily confused because they are spelled similarly or because they sound alike. These words have different definitions, so you need to be sure you use the correct one.

abroad aboard	all together altogether	breath breathe	ever every	of off	trail trial
accuse excuse	angel angle	cloth clothe	expect suspect	picture pitcher	use used
advice advise	any more anymore	costume custom	farther further	quiet quite	weather whether
affect effect	any way anyway	dairy diary	lay lie	recent resent	were where
all ready already	bean been	desert dessert	loose lose	though through	your you're

Now turn to page 241 to practice spelling commonly confused words correctly.

Common Core State Standards Literacy Handbook

Name _____

Spelling Commonly Confused Words Correctly

Practice

Write a story about a real or imaginary pet. Use some problem words and some easily confused words in your story.

Underline each problem word and easily confused word you use. Then check to be sure you have used and spelled it correctly.

_____

_____

_____

_____

_____

_____

_____

_____

_____

_____

_____

_____

_____

_____

_____

_____

_____

Standard
3.a

Lesson A
Use Precise Language Effectively

Good writers and effective speakers choose their words very carefully so that they precisely describe the idea or topic they are explaining. Word choice can have a powerful effect on your message.

Compare these paragraphs. Which one describes the scene more precisely?

> *The boys sat on the bench and waited for the bus. Finally it came. They got on and walked to the back. They sat down and looked out the window. They had a long ride ahead of them before they got home.*
>
> *The boys slouched on the rusty bench and waited for the bus. Finally, it chugged up the hill to their stop. They trudged up the stairs and sauntered down the narrow aisle towards the back. They slid into the cracked plastic seats and stared out the window. The ride home would be long and tedious.*

The words the writer chose for the second paragraph are more vivid and describe the actions of the boys, the motion of the bus, and other details more precisely. These word choices help readers picture what is happening.

Now look carefully at the words that tell the actions. Compare the word choices. Why is the word *slouched* a more effective word choice than *sat*? Find other word pairs that mean the same thing but one is more precise.

> The boys <u>sat</u> on the bench and waited for the bus. Finally it <u>came</u>. They <u>got on</u> and <u>walked</u> to the back. They <u>sat down</u> and <u>looked</u> out the window. They had a long ride ahead of them before they got home.
>
> The boys <u>slouched</u> on the rusty bench and waited for the bus. Finally, it <u>chugged</u> up the hill to their stop. They <u>trudged</u> up the stairs and <u>sauntered</u> down the narrow aisle towards the back. They <u>slid</u> into the cracked plastic seats and <u>stared</u> out the window. The ride home would be long and tedious.

Now turn to page 244 to practice using precise words and phrases effectively.

Name _____

Use Precise Language Effectively

Practice

Read the sentences below. Then rewrite the sentences by replacing the underlined words with more precise language.

1. The police officer <u>walked</u> down the street.

_____

2. The woman helped the <u>little</u> girl.

_____

3. The new puppy <u>ran</u> around the backyard.

_____

4. We <u>had a nice time</u> at the party.

_____

5. My friend <u>talked to</u> children about bike safety.

_____

6. We <u>walked</u> in the holiday parade.

_____

7. Dorothy and Rick and <u>went for a ride on the fast boat.</u>

_____

8. Aunt Kathy admired the <u>pretty</u> painting.

_____

9. Joe thought the chicken dish <u>tasted good</u>.

_____

10. The race cars <u>drove</u> around the racetrack.

_____

Lesson B
Choose Punctuation for Effect

Punctuation is like road signs for written language. It lets readers know such things as when to stop, when to pause, and what the exact words of a speaker are. We follow the rules for using punctuation so our readers can clearly understand our writing.

But did you know that punctuation can also be used for effect? When we write, we can use punctuation to show emotion or to create a desired tone.

Choose Punctuation for Effect

- Use **parentheses ( )** around material that is added to a sentence but is not important to the meaning of the sentence.

  > *My pesky little sister gets her way when she whines (always).*

- Put punctuation inside the parentheses when it goes with the information inside.

  > *I will perform in my first school play tonight. (Yikes!)*

- Put punctuation outside the parentheses when it goes with the main part of the sentence.

  > *I have to go to the dentist tomorrow (I think).*

- Use a **dash** to add emphasis to your writing. A dash is a mark of separation. It is stronger than a comma and more relaxed than parentheses.

  > *This is Jill—the nicest person I've ever met!*
  > *I'm not looking forward to going to the dentist—especially if she finds a cavity.*

- An **interjection** is a word or a phrase that shows emotion.

- Use a comma to separate interjections from the rest of a sentence.

> Yes, I want to go to the party with you!

- If the interjection shows a very strong emotion, use an exclamation mark.

> Oh no! I forgot to turn the stove off.

Now turn to pages 247–248 to practice choosing punctuation for effect.

Name _____

Choose Punctuation for Effect 1

Practice

Proofread the sentences. Add parentheses ( ) once in each numbered item.

1. Please sign the permission slip see the attachment.

2. The mural will take up one whole wall. Wow!

3. Mara and some other students will go with our teacher to the paint store I can't go.

4. Our mural won't have words. Yeah!

5. It will be all pictures which is good for me.

6. The mural will show Are you surprised? things that we do at school.

7. Each grade of the five grades at my school will do one section.

8. Look at my sketch found below of what I want to draw.

Name _____

Choose Punctuation for Effect 2

Practice

Add commas after the interjections and dashes where needed.

1. Yes we learned that many plants and animals have disappeared from our national parks.

2. Oh did you know that elk have been reintroduced to the Great Smoky Mountains National Park in North Carolina?

3. There was a time a long time when no elk were in North Carolina.

4. There were fewer plants for small animals to eat and fewer small animals for big animals to eat it must have been terrible for the animals

5. Some elk 28 total were reintroduced into the national park.

6. The researchers have been studying the elk thankfully.

7. Yes the researchers can tell how the elk are doing.

8. The study was very promising 11 baby elk were born.

9. Wow that is wonderful!

10. Yes the researchers are hoping that the natural balance will be restored to the park.

Lesson C
Levels of Language

We speak and write differently depending on the situation. We adjust our levels of language depending on whom we are talking to and what the occasion is. For example, we use formal English when we are requesting information from a business or someone we don't know. If we are speaking with a friend, we would use informal English. In this lesson, you will learn more about formal and informal English and when we use them.

Using Formal English

Formal English is used mainly in writing and in some speaking situations. This style of English has a more serious tone and is commonly used in reports, essays, business letters, and conversations with people we may know but are not close friends with.

- Formal English uses more complex vocabulary than informal English. It uses words that you probably wouldn't use in a regular conversation with a friend.

- When formal English is used in writing, sentences are usually longer and more complex than when you are writing to a friend.

- People also use formal English when speaking in formal situations, such as during a job interview or when talking to the principal.

- A **business letter** is a letter you write to a company, a businessperson, or someone in the government. Business letters use more formal language than friendly letters.

2639 Clearwood Cove
Little Rock, Arkansas 72201
January 3, 2011

Ms. Sarah Rodriguez
Ever Clean Recycling
1136 Haywood Suite 63
Little Rock, Arkansas 72205

Dear Ms. Rodriguez:

    I am interested in starting an aluminum-recycling program for my school. Our cafeteria serves juice in aluminum cans, and it is the most popular beverage. I understand you offer programs for schools, and I am interested in getting some information on these programs.

    If you would like to call me, my telephone number is 555-6367, or you can e-mail me at joeh@xyz.com.

Your truly,

Joseph Herrera

Now turn to page 251 to practice using formal language.

Name _____

Formal Language

Practice

Write a business letter to a local professional, such as a doctor, scientist, or lawyer. Invite him or her to speak to your class about a specific topic. You may change any of the information below. Make sure you use formal language as you write your letter.

345 Mica Lane
New York, NY 10980
November 7, 2011

Dr. Edward Dahme
Humana Hospital
New York, NY 10980
Dear Dr. Dahme:

_____

_____

_____

_____

_____

_____

_____

_____

_____

_____

_____

_____

Using Informal English

People often use **informal English** when they are speaking to friends and family. People also use informal English when they write e-mails, notes, and letters to people they know.

- When people write informal English, they use everyday vocabulary and sometimes include expressions and slang that is common where they live. For instance, in informal English, a writer might use the word *stuff* to describe something he or she found rather than a specific name.

- Informal English often uses personal pronouns, such as *I, you*, and *we*, to create a more personal style than formal English. Contractions, such as *it's* instead of *it is*, are also very common.

- Friends and family members often send one another e-mails. In these e-mails, writers use informal English.

Dear Johanna,

What a day! My dad and I had to take three different planes to make it all the way up to the camp we'll be staying! We finally made it this morning. It's so cool here! The cabin we're staying in is pretty small, but it's right by a huge lake. There's also a cabin where we get to chow down at meal time. The food here is awesome.

My dad and I spent the morning getting our fishing gear ready. There is a lot of stuff you need to go fishing. You should see my dad's tackle box! He has fake frogs, fish, and these gross rubber worms in there. We're going try our luck at fishing after lunch. Maybe I'll catch the big one!

Anyway, I just wanted to say hello. Did I miss anything fun at home? I wish you were here with us. Tell Tony and Gina I say hello, and write back soon!

Liza

Now turn to page 253 to practice using informal language.

Name _____

Using Informal English

Practice

Write an e-mail to a friend or family member. Tell that person about something that happened to you recently. You can tell about something that happened at school, at home, or somewhere else. Make sure you use informal English as you write your e-mail.

_____

_____

_____

_____

_____

_____

_____

_____

_____

_____

_____

_____

_____

_____

_____

_____

_____

Standard
4

Lesson A
Multiple-Meaning Words

A **multiple-meaning word** is a word that has more than one meaning. Though the word's meaning, part of speech, and pronunciation may change according to how it is used in a sentence, the spelling of the word stays the same.

A **Homonym** is one example of a multiple-meaning word. Homonyms are words that are spelled the same and pronounced the same but have different meanings.

A **Homograph** is another example of a multiple-meaning word. Homographs are words that are spelled the same but have different meanings and origins. They may also have different pronunciations.

Homonyms

Read the following sentence pairs, looking closely at the underlined homonyms.

1. Sam did a <u>fine</u> job on his book report.
   You will have to pay a <u>fine</u> if you are late returning the library book.

The word *fine* is spelled and pronounced the same in both sentences, but its meaning is different. In the first sentence, *fine* is an adjective that means "very good." In the second sentence, *fine* is a noun that means "penalty."

2. The musicians followed the directions of the <u>conductor</u> throughout the concert.
   We bought our tickets on the train from the <u>conductor</u>.

In the first sentence, "followed the directions" helps you understand that a conductor is someone who leads musicians. In the second sentence, you can see that this kind of conductor is someone who collects train fares.

3. My <u>paddle</u> broke during the ping-pong game, so I had no way to hit the ball.
   We will <u>paddle</u> down the river in a canoe.

In the first sentence, you can see that a paddle is a thing (and therefore a noun) used to hit ping-pong balls. In the second sentence, you can see that *paddle* refers to the action (and is therefore a verb) by which a canoe is moved.

Homographs

Read the following sentences. Note the underlined homographs.

1. Local farmers <u>produce</u> and sell fresh <u>produce</u> at the market.

The first *produce* is a verb meaning "grow," and the second *produce* is a noun meaning "fruits and vegetables." The two words have different pronunciations, too.

2. The <u>desert</u> in the Southwest is full of cactuses and other plants found in dry climates.
   The mother bird guards the baby birds and does not <u>desert</u> them.

In the first sentence, "dry climates" gives you the clue that a desert is a type of dry land area. In the second sentence, "not" tells you that *desert* means the opposite of *guard*. These two words are also pronounced in different ways.

3. To save water, turn the <u>tap</u> off while you brush your teeth.
   <u>Tap</u> the hard-boiled egg gently with a spoon to crack the shell.

In the first sentence, "to save water" and "turn . . . off" tell you that *tap* (a noun) is another word for *faucet*. In the second sentence, "gently" and "with a spoon" lead you to understand that here *tap* is a verb that means "to strike lightly." *Tap* is pronounced the same in both sentences.

You can use a dictionary to find all the meanings and pronunciations of a word. Then you can use context clues to choose the correct meaning of the word as it is used in a sentence.

Now turn to pages 256–257 to practice using multiple-meaning words.

Name _____

Multiple-Meaning Words
Practice

> **pick** verb **1.** to select or choose. Pick a card from the deck. **2.** to gather with the fingers. We picked blueberries for a pie. **3.** to pull at and let go; pluck. She picked the strings on the banjo. noun **1.** a tool with a wooden handle and a metal head, used for breaking rocks and loosening dirt. He used a pick to break the rocks into chunks. **2.** a thin piece of metal or plastic used for playing a stringed instrument. I bought a new pick at the guitar shop. **3.** the best of something. The prize cow is the pick of the herd.

A. Use the model dictionary entry to answer the questions about the homonyms.

1. I think she will pick the red shirt instead of the blue one.

Is pick a noun or a verb in this sentence?_____

What is the meaning of *pick* here?_____

2. The miner's pick was worn down from much use._____

Is pick a noun or a verb in this sentence? _____

What is the meaning of *pick* here? _____

3. We will pick vegetables from the garden for a salad.

Is pick a noun or a verb in this sentence? _____

What is the meaning of *pick* here? _____

Name _____

B. Use a dictionary to find the meanings of the following homographs. Then write a sentence for each meaning of the word.

1. content _____

content _____

2. well _____

well _____

3. object _____

object _____

4. stoop _____

stoop _____

5. dove _____

dove _____

Standard
4

Lesson B
Use Context Clues

Context clues can help you figure out the meaning of a word or phrase you don't know. These clues can be found in the words and sentences surrounding the unknown word or phrase.

Sometimes a writer uses **signal words** that indicate a certain type of context clue. You will learn to recognize different types of context clues you might come across as you read.

Look at the model below.

Context Clues: Model

The chart below shows different types of context clues you might come across as you read.

Kinds of Context Clues		
Clue: Definitions	**Clue: Examples**	**Clue: Restatements**
Does the writer define the word? Words such as *means* or *is* may signal a definition.	Does the writer give examples of the word? *Such as* and *other* may signal examples.	Does the writer restate the word? Look for signal words such as *which is* and *or*.
word: *fuel*	word: *materials*	word: *genealogy*
Today we learned that a fuel is a <u>source of energy</u>.	The artist used materials such as <u>chalk and clay</u>.	Mom studies our genealogy, or <u>family history</u>.

Definitions, examples, and restatements can all be used as context clues.

Use Definitions as Context Clues

Look at the underlined words in the model sentences. The double-underlined words **define** the underlined words. Signal words for definitions include *is* and *means.*

A border is something that separates one thing from another.

The noise of the wind is ceaseless, which means that it never stops.

Yesterday's concert in the park was a great musical performance.

Use Examples as Context Clues

Look at the underlined words or phrases in the model sentences. The double-underlined words are **examples** of the underlined words. Some words that signal examples are *such as, other, include, these,* and *for example.*

Nocturnal animals, such as bats and owls look for food after dark.

The fledglings in our yard include baby wrens and baby robins.

Skyscrapers and other tall buildings are in many cities.

Use Restatements as Context Clues

Look at the underlined words or phrases in the model sentences. The double-underlined words are **restatements** of the underlined words. Words that signal restatements include *or, that is, in other words,* and *which is.*

Snakes slither, or slide along the ground.

It is beneficial to get eight hours of sleep; that is, it has a good effect.

I was in a hurry, so I told my friend to cut to the chase; in other words, to get to the point of his story.

Now turn to pages 260–261 to practice using context clues.

6

Name _____

Use Context Clues

Practice

Definitions

Circle the words in each sentence that define the underlined word.

1. Shredded cheese is cheese that has been torn into tiny strips.

2. The theme of the story is the author's message.

3. Animals that hunt other animals for food are predators.

4. A city is an urban area.

5. Conservation involves the preservation of natural resources.

Examples

Circle the words in each sentence that serve as examples of the underlined word.

1. The queen's treasure included gold, silver, and jewels.

2. We packed soup, crackers, and other provisions for our camping trip.

3. Resources such as wind and water are used to make electricity.

4. Zelda bought school supplies such as pens and notebooks.

5. The terrain of a forest may include trees, creeks, and rocks.

Name _____

Restatements

A. Circle the words in each sentence that serve as restatements of the underlined word.

1. The stories tell of great deeds, which are the actions of heroes.

2. Many species, or kinds, of insect live in that field.

3. Pioneers settled the open range, or empty land, of the West.

B. Complete each sentence below by restating the underlined word. You may use a dictionary to help you.

1. The plant's remains had decayed over time; in other words, they had

   _____

2. Drinking water is crucial, or _____,

   to our survival.

Understand Word Parts

Many English words are formed by adding prefixes and suffixes to a root word. Prefixes, suffixes, and roots often come from Latin and Greek.

Prefixes

A **prefix** is a word part that is added to the beginning of a word to change its meaning. The chart shows some common Latin and Greek prefixes and their meanings.

Latin Prefix	Meaning
pre-	before
sub-	under
in-/im-	not

Greek Prefix	Meaning
anti-	against
dia-	between, across
en-/em-	in, within

Read the sentences below. The meaning of each underlined word can be determined by thinking about the meaning of the prefix.

When Spencer turned three, he started <u>preschool</u>.

Preschool means "before school." This is a place where young children go before they are old enough for school.

We rode the <u>subway</u> train in New York City.

Subway means "underground way." This kind of train runs underground.

The <u>anticruelty</u> society works to protect animals.

Anticruelty means "against cruelty." This group wants to stop cruelty, or unkindness, to animals.

For more information about prefixes, go to Foundational Skills 3.1 Lesson A **Prefixes** on Volume 1 page 197.

Now turn to page 263 to practice using what you know about prefixes.

Name _____

Prefixes

Practice

Read each sentence. Use what you know about prefixes to write the meaning of each boldfaced word.

1. Lily enjoys watching previews of new movies.

   _____

2. The submarine traveled along the ocean floor.

   _____

3. My turtle is incapable of moving fast.

   _____

4. Our antipollution principal encourages us to ride our bikes to school.

   _____

5. As they get older, children become more independent.

   _____

6. She drew a diagonal line from one corner of the square to another.

   _____

7. We gathered in the gym for a pregame pep rally today.

   _____

8. The police enforce the town's laws.

   _____

9. Long ago, people thought air travel was impossible.

   _____

10. Make sure you wash your cut with antibacterial soap.

   _____

Suffixes

A **suffix** is a word part that is added to the end of a word to change its meaning. The chart shows some common Latin and Greek suffixes and their meanings.

Latin Prefix	Meaning
-able/-ible	able to, worthy of
-er/-or	one who
-fy/-ify	to make

Greek Prefix	Meaning
-log/-logue	to speak
-ist	one who
-ize	to make

Read the sentences below. The meaning of each underlined word can be determined by thinking about the meaning of the suffix.

Gymnasts are very <u>flexible</u>.

Flexible means "able to flex." When you think about how *flex* means "bend," you can see that *flexible* means "able to bend."

Her work as an <u>artist</u> involves watercolors.

Because *-ist* means "one who," an artist is someone who creates art.

We brought tablets on our camping trip to <u>purify</u> our water.

Purify means "to make pure." The tablets make water pure, or clean and safe for drinking.

For more information about prefixes, go to 3.1 Lesson A **Multisyllabic Words Suffixes** on Volume 1 page 199.

Now turn to page 265 to practice using what you know about suffixes.

Name _____

Suffixes

Practice

A. Look at the boldfaced phrases. Use what you know about suffixes to write one word that means the same as the entire boldfaced phrase.

1. **A person who travels** across time is a time _____

2. **A person who mines** for gold is a _____

3. **A person who sails ships** is a _____

4. **A person who gets a degree** in biology is a _____

5. **A person who survives** a shipwreck is a _____

B. Underline the suffix in each word below. Then write the meaning of each word on the lines provided.

1. dialogue _____

2. likable _____

3. beautify _____

4. harmonize _____

5. travelogue _____

Roots

The **root** of a word is its basic meaning before a prefix or a suffix is added to it. If you know the spellings and meanings of roots, you can figure out how to spell and define words that contain them. Here are some common Latin and Greek roots and their meanings.

Latin Root	Meaning
port	carry
aud	hear
duc	lead, make
script	write

Greek Root	Meaning
tele	far
photo	light
graph	write
auto	self

Read the sentences below. The meaning of each underlined word can be determined by thinking about the meaning of its root.

I can transport my science project from home to school on my bike.

Transport, containing the root *port,* means "to carry from one place to another."

The inscription over its front door tells the year the school was built.

Inscription, containing the root *script,* means "something that is written as a record."

People used to send messages by telegraph.

Telegraph, which is made from the roots *tele* and *graph,* refers to a machine used for communication between places that are far apart.

Now turn to page 267 to practice using what you know about word roots.

Name _____

Roots

Practice

A. Complete each sentence with a word from the box that takes the place of the underlined words.

> | autograph | portable | conduct | photograph | audience |

1. Fans often ask the movie star for her <u>signature</u>. _____

2. Dad sent a holiday <u>picture</u> of our family to relatives. _____

3. Is that television <u>light enough to be carried</u>? _____

4. When the concert ended, the <u>people listening</u> clapped. _____

5. Rangers <u>lead</u> tours in our national parks. _____

B. Look at the roots of the words in the box: auto, graph, port, duc, photo, and aud. Choose one root and then think of another word that contains it. Write a sentence of your own using the new word.

_____

_____

_____

Lesson D
Use Print and Digital Resources

Reference materials are printed texts or online resources that give factual information about a word or a topic. **Dictionaries, glossaries,** and **thesauruses** are examples of reference materials you can use to learn about words.

Dictionaries and Glossaries

Dictionaries and glossaries give lots of information about words. You can use a print or digital *dictionary* to look up any word that you would like to know more about. You can use a *glossary,* which is found in the back of a print book or as a link in an e-book (also called a digital book), to look up key words used in that book.

Entry

The words listed in a dictionary or glossary are called entries. They are in bold type and alphabetical order.

Pronunciation

An entry word is followed by its pronunciation, or the way it is spoken. The pronunciation is broken into syllables, and accent marks show which syllables to emphasize.

Part of Speech and Definitions

A word's part of speech and definitions follow its pronunciation. Multiple definitions are numbered, and the most common meanings are usually listed first.

Sample Sentences

Some dictionaries and glossaries give sample sentences so you can see how a word is used. Pictures may also be included to help you understand word meanings.

Look at the sample dictionary entry below. Note the entry word, the pronunciation, the part of speech, the definitions, and the sample sentences.

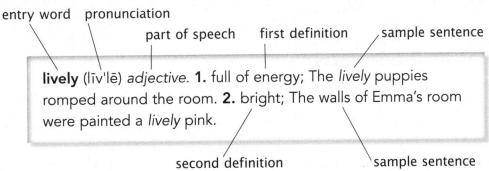

Now look at this glossary entry. You can see how similar it is to a dictionary entry. One difference is that the glossary entry includes the page number where the word is located in the book. Another difference is that only the definition of the word as it is used in the book is included.

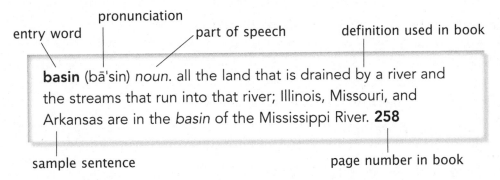

Now turn to pages 270–271 to practice using dictionary and glossary entries.

6

Name _____

Dictionaries and Glossaries

Practice

> **distort** (di stôrt′) verb. **1.** to twist the meaning of something; The reporter *distorts* what people say. **2.** to twist out of shape; The mirror *distorts* my face when I look into it.

A. Use the dictionary entry above to answer these questions. Write a or b.

1. Which meaning of distort do you find in the following sentence?

Eduardo twisted the hanger and distorted its shape. _____

    a. Meaning #1   **b.** Meaning #2

2. True or false? The word distort has two syllables. _____

    a. true   **b.** false

3. To pronounce *distort*, do you emphasize the first syllable or the second? _____

    a. first   **b.** second

Name _____

B. To link to a part of a digital glossary, follow the steps below. Find the word stress in the glossary and then answer the following questions.

1. Type in your *Common Core State Standards Literacy eHandbook* address into your browser's address bar.

2. Click on Part 6: Language in the first Table of Contents.

3. Go to 6.3 Vocabulary Acquisition and Use in the Second Table of Contents.

4. Click on Lesson D Use Print and Digital Resources

5. Click on Dictionaries and Glossaries.

6. Click on Practice.

7. Click on Digital Glossary.

Digital Glossary

1. What part of speech is the word *stress* as it is defined in this glossary entry?

   _____

2. What are the entries above and below the word *stress*?

   _____

3. The word *stress* can also be a noun. Use *stress* as a noun in a sentence of your own.

   _____

   _____

Thesauruses

A print or digital **thesaurus** is a reference that is similar to a dictionary. Instead of giving definitions, however, a thesaurus lists **Synonyms** for words. Synonyms are words that have the same (or nearly the same) meaning. In order to be considered synonyms, the words must be the same part of speech. For example, the words *guardian* and *protector* are synonyms. Knowing synonyms for unfamiliar words can help you understand and remember them.

Some thesauruses also list **Antonyms** for words. Antonyms are words that have opposite meanings. In order to be considered antonyms, the words must be the same part of speech. For example, *safe* and *dangerous* are antonyms.

Some print thesauruses have an **index** that tells you the entry number where you can find the word. The index also helps you decide which meaning of the word would be best. For example, you may look up the word *little* in an index and find this:

little   **-in quantity**   **53**

           -in size   **187**

Since you are looking for a word to describe the size of something, you turn to entry 187. There you find the word *little* listed with several synonyms. You choose *puny* as the perfect word for your size description.

Now study the sample thesaurus entry below. Imagine that you are reading about someone who has a *buoyant* personality. You find *buoyant* in the dictionary and learn that it means "cheerful." You want to find synonyms for *buoyant,* so you look it up in a thesaurus and find this:

buoyant   **-floating**   **312**

             -hopeful   **872**

Because *hopeful* is closer in meaning to *cheerful,* you turn to page 872 to find a list of synonyms for this meaning of buoyant.

Now turn to page 273 to practice using a thesaurus.

Name _____

Thesauruses

Practice

Replace each word in parentheses with a synonym from the box below. Use a print or digital thesaurus to help you.

| clumsy | nimble | announced | meddle | certain |

1. "Don't (interfere) _____ with my plans to be king of the road!"

2. The roadrunner was (awkward) _____ when he first tried to run and jump.

3. He was (convinced) _____ he could not learn.

4. Later, when the roadrunner danced in circles, you could see how (agile) _____ he had become.

5. "The roadrunner is our hero!" the animals (proclaimed) _____.

Lesson E
Understand Figurative Language

Figurative language is language that goes beyond the literal, dictionary meaning of the words. Some examples of figurative language are called figures of speech. Writers use figures of speech to help create pictures in their readers' minds. In this lesson, you will learn about two figures of speech: **simile** and **metaphor.**

A simile compares two things that are not alike by using the words *like* or *as*. A metaphor compares two things that are not alike but without using *like* or *as*.

Similes	Both	Metaphors
▪ Use the word *like* or *as* to signal the comparison Example: The cat's eyes glowed in the dark like fiery coals.	▪ Compare two unlike things ▪ Help readers picture what is being described ▪ May relate unfamiliar things to familiar things	▪ State that one thing is the other; do not use *like* or *as* Example: The cat's eyes were fiery coals in the dark.

Similes

Similes can help you figure out the meanings of words that you do not know. In similes, those words are compared to something you might know. Look at these examples, and note that all contain either *like* or *as*.

The barge eased through the canal *like* a knife slicing through warm butter.

• You could understand the meaning of *eased* by picturing how simple it is to cut through warm butter.

The river shimmered *as* if jewels were beneath the water.

• You could understand the meaning of *shimmered* by thinking of words that describe jewels, such as *sparkle, glitter, shine,* and so on.

Because the wind was so strong, the seagulls had to walk sideways *like* crabs.

- The meaning of *sideways* becomes clearer when you think about how crabs move.

As a result of the drought, the ground was dry *as* a lizard's skin.

- The sentence itself lets you know that *drought* is connected to "dry ground," but the image of the lizard's skin helps you understand that *drought* has to do with severe dryness and lack of rain.

Metaphors

Writers use metaphors to help readers better understand what is being described. A metaphor states that one thing *is* the other. Read the following metaphor:

Frank's excited little sister was a spinning top.

What do you think of when you picture a spinning top? Most likely, you picture something that is constantly in motion. If Frank's sister is a spinning top, it means that she is showing her excitement by moving around a lot.

Below are more examples of metaphors. Think about how each metaphor triggers you to use a particular sense. By using your senses, you can better understand what the writer wants you to feel about what is being described.

The dancers at the festival are a rainbow of colors.

- This metaphor helps you <u>see</u> the dancers.

The baby's laughter was the sweet song of birds.

- This metaphor helps you <u>hear</u> the baby's laughter.

The clean house is springtime fresh.

- This metaphor helps you <u>smell</u> the clean house.

The wool scarf was sandpaper against my neck.

- This metaphor helps you <u>feel</u> the scarf.

The loss of the baseball game is sour milk in my mouth.

- This metaphor helps you <u>taste</u> the loss.

Now turn to page 276–278 to practice understanding figurative language.

Name _____

Similes

Practice

A. Complete these sentences. Choose words that would help readers picture what is being described.

1. The pillow was as soft as _____

2. The man's kind words were like _____

3. His heart pounded like _____

4. The wind howled as loud as a _____

B. Follow the directions in order to write your own similes.

1. Make a list of things that have curves. _____

   Now write a simile that could help someone picture a very curvy road.

   _____

2. Make a list of things that move very quickly. _____

   Now write a simile to help someone see a person running at top speed.

   _____

   _____

C. Follow the directions below.

1. Explain this simile in your own words: *The garden looked as pretty as a picture.*

   _____

   _____

2. Write your own sentence using this simile: *as light as a feather.*

   _____

   _____

Name _____

Metaphors

Practice

A. On the lines below, write sentences that use metaphors. Use the examples in the organizer for guidance. Think of how an example could help someone understand what you are trying to describe. One sentence has been done for you.

Sense	Example 1	Example 2	Example 3	Example 4	Example 5
Sight	a garden in bloom	a quilt	a burned building	a traffic jam	clouds
Hearing	a thunderclap	water running	a fast-moving train	a machine humming	popcorn popping
Taste	your favorite food	bitter medicine	hot sauce	honey	sweet juice
Smell	a rotten fruit	a rose	bread baking	soap	vinegar
Touch	a soft blanket	warm sunshine	a snake's skin	**ice**	silk

1. Her skin was **ice** after being outside without a coat.

2. _____

3. _____

4. _____

5. _____

Name _____

B. Follow the directions below.

1. Explain this metaphor in your own words: *The lake was a mirror.*

2. Write your own sentence using a metaphor to relate stars to diamonds.

_____

_____

Lesson F
Understand Common Expressions and Sayings

Idioms, adages, and proverbs are types of common expressions and sayings that have meanings beyond what can be understood by their individual words.

An **idiom** is an expression common to a particular culture that does not mean what it literally says. You have to learn the meanings of idioms, just like you learn the meanings of words. For example, the idiom to *play it by ear* means "to do something without planning."

A **proverb** is a statement of practical wisdom expressed in a simple way. An example of a proverb is "Beauty is skin deep," which means that someone's appearance doesn't tell you what he or she is really like. An **adage** is a well-known proverb that has been used for a long time. An example of an adage would be "Actions speak louder than words," which means that doing something is more effective than just talking about it. Adages and proverbs are so closely related that the terms are often used interchangeably.

Idioms

There are different ways to figure out the meaning of an **idiom.** Sometimes you can find hints by reading around the idiom. Look at the words leading up to the underlined idiom.

After hours of gardening, Mia was tired. She decided to call it a day, so she put her tools away and went inside the house.

From the context, you can tell that *call it a day* means "to stop or finish something."

Sometimes an idiom can be found in a dictionary under its main word. The main word in this underlined idiom is *thumb.*

"I am all thumbs today," she said with a sigh.

At the end of the dictionary entry for *thumb,* you can see that the idiom *all thumbs* means "awkward or clumsy."

Finally, sometimes you just have to ask for the meaning of an idiom. As you learn and remember new idioms, your knowledge of their meanings will build over time.

I got <u>cold feet</u> when it was time to perform in the play.

If someone gets cold feet before an activity or event, it means the person is nervous about it and hesitates to go through with it.

Now turn to page 281 to practice using what you know about idioms.

Name _____

Idioms

Practice

A. Read each idiom. Write what you think it means on the line next to it. The first one has been done for you.

1. music to my ears _____ something that sounds pleasant _____

2. keep your eyes peeled _____

3. she was all smiles _____

4. he has a nose for news _____

5. keep a stiff upper lip _____

6. face the music _____

7. keep your chin up _____

B. Circle the meaning of the underlined idiom.

1. The news came <u>out of the blue</u>, so Isaac was shocked.

    a. suddenly   **b.** out of the sky

2. The meeting was almost over when Janet said, "Let's <u>wind up</u> by six o'clock."

    a. change time on the clock   **b.** finish the task

3. Zachary was rarely sick, so his teacher was surprised to hear that he was <u>under the weather.</u>

    a. lying under a cloud   **b.** unwell

Adages and Proverbs

Adages and **proverbs** offer advice and observations about life. You can build your knowledge of adages and proverbs by asking someone what they mean or by looking them up online. Read these examples of adages and proverbs.

Don't judge a book by its cover . . . *means* . . .
Don't judge something based on its appearance alone.

Look before you leap . . . *means* . . .
Think about something before rushing into it.

Practice makes perfect . . . *means* . . .
Doing something over and over again will help you to get better at it.

Better safe than sorry . . . *means* . . .
Take the time to be careful doing something so that there are no bad results.

Too many cooks spoil the broth . . . *means* . . .
If too many people try to do the same job, the job will not be done well.

Now turn to page 283 to practice using what you know about adages and proverbs.

Name _____

Adages and Proverbs

Practice

Underline the adage or proverb in each sentence, and then circle the correct meaning.

1. We use coupons when we buy our groceries, because a penny saved is a penny earned.

    a. Holding on to money you already have is as useful as getting more of it.

    b. It is hard to save money without using coupons.

2. Knowing that a picture paints a thousand words, I mailed a photograph of my baseball trophy to my grandmother.

    a. Photographs are always more interesting than letters.

    b. One picture of something can tell as much about it as a written description.

3. My sister helped me with my homework, so I helped her with her chores; after all, one good turn deserves another.

    a. You should do a favor for someone who has done a favor for you.

    b. Turning in homework on time is helpful to the teacher.

4. We will clean the house more quickly if we do it together, because many hands make light work.

    a. If a lot of people work together on something, the task will be easier.

    b. If a lot of people work together on something, the task will get done before dark.

5. Even though I gave my friend a present the week after her birthday, I figured it was better late than never.

    a. If your friends forget your birthday, you should not give them presents.

    b. It is better to do something late than to not do it at all.

Lesson G
Understand Word Relationships

Understanding synonyms and antonyms helps you build your vocabulary by relating new words to words you might already know. You can use a thesaurus to find synonyms—and often antonyms—for words. A dictionary is another tool for finding synonyms and antonyms.

Synonyms are words that have the same, or nearly the same, meaning. In order to be considered synonyms, two words must be the same part of speech. For example, in the sentence below, the verbs *destroyed* and *ruined* are synonyms.

The hurricane <u>destroyed</u> several buildings and <u>ruined</u> the power lines.

Antonyms are words that have opposite meanings. In order to be antonyms, two words must be the same part of speech. Words like *but, not, on the other hand, instead of,* and *rather* often signal that an antonym might be used in the text. For example, in the sentence below, the adjectives *humid* and *dry* are antonyms.

Some people dislike hot <u>humid</u> weather but enjoy the <u>dry</u> heat of the desert.

Synonyms

Read the story below to see how one student uses synonyms to build her vocabulary.

Ariana is trying to find out more about her Greek heritage. While reading about Greek foods, she finds a description of tzatziki, a Greek sauce. She is confused when she sees an unknown word, underlined below, that describes the sauce.

Tzatziki is a <u>delectable</u> sauce that plays a big part in many Greek meals.

Ariana knows that sauces add flavor to meals, so she creates a concept web and adds possible synonyms for *delectable* in it. She adds words based on what she herself likes about sauces.

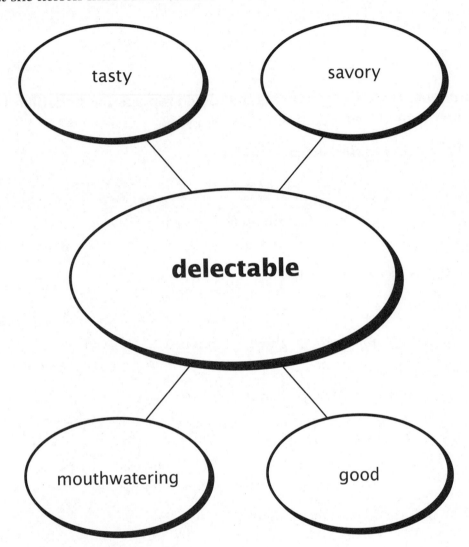

Ariana uses one of her synonyms to replace *delectable* so that she can better understand how the words are related.

Tzatziki is <u>tasty</u> sauce that plays a big part in many Greek meals.

Now turn to page 286–287 to practice using what you know about synonyms.

Name _____

Synonyms

Practice

A. For each sentence, circle the synonyms that could replace the underlined word. You may use a thesaurus or a dictionary to help you.

1. Danica and Ronny <u>cleaned</u> the kitchen after dinner.

tidied	swept	messed	straightened	painted	left

2. Carmine <u>threw</u> his suitcase into the trunk.

built	tossed	bounced	glued	pitched	heaved

3. Tareq <u>smiled</u> when Rodrigo said he got the answer right.

frowned	grinned	beamed	grimaced	bowed	grunted

4. Su Yi didn't like the <u>odor</u> in the school cafeteria.

menu	scent	racket	mood	aroma	smell

5. The cool breeze and the warm sun made the picnic very <u>pleasant</u>.

nice	crowded	agreeable	lengthy	enjoyable	gloomy

Common Core State Standards Literacy Handbook

Name _____

B. You can better understand unfamiliar words by relating them to familiar words with similar meanings. Look at the underlined words in the passage. There are synonyms for these words in the passage. Find the synonyms and write them on the lines below.

Today's game was a <u>triumph</u> for our unlucky baseball team. It was the first win for the team in four <u>consecutive</u> seasons! We couldn't believe we had won after losing so many years straight. Several hits should have been <u>difficult</u> to catch, but for some reason it was not hard for us to field the balls today. We are no longer a group of <u>unfortunate</u> players; we are a team of <u>elated</u> stars! Our coach and fans are also happy for us. We're looking forward to next season!

1. triumph _____

2. consecutive _____

3. difficult _____

4. unfortunate _____

5. elated _____

Antonyms

Read this passage to see how using antonyms can help you figure out what a word means.

One of the first steam engines was built to solve a problem. In the 1600s, mines were dug very deeply and underground water poured into them. The flooded mines eventually had to be <u>abandoned</u>. But mine owners thought the mines could still be used if the water was pumped out. Thus a steam engine was invented to help remove the water from the mines.

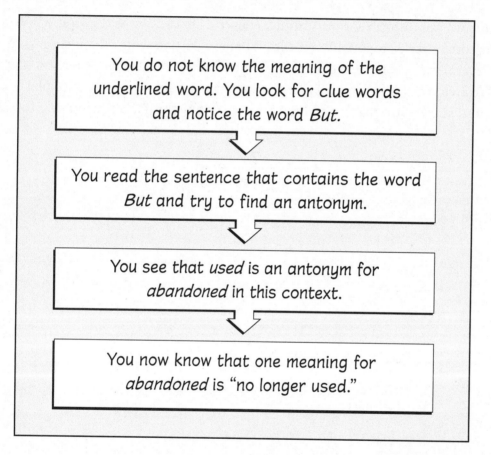

You do not know the meaning of the underlined word. You look for clue words and notice the word *But*.

You read the sentence that contains the word *But* and try to find an antonym.

You see that *used* is an antonym for *abandoned* in this context.

You now know that one meaning for *abandoned* is "no longer used."

Now turn to page 289 to practice using what you know about antonyms.

Name _____

Antonyms

Practice

A. Draw a line from each word in column 1 to its antonym in column 2.

Column 1
1. selfish
2. villain
3. polite
4. brittle
5. anxious

Column 2
a. hero
b. serene
c. flexible
d. giving
e. rude

B. In the blank, write an antonym for each underlined word.

1. My dad was <u>overjoyed</u> when he saw my report card. _____

2. The fabric of the cushion felt very <u>silky</u>. _____

3. The light in the room was <u>dim</u>. _____

4. Thalia made a fruit salad with very <u>tart</u> cherries. _____

5. I looked out the window and saw <u>dreary</u> skies. _____

Lesson H
Build Vocabulary

As you read, you use vocabulary strategies to figure out the meanings of unfamiliar words. Once you understand new words, you can use them when writing and speaking.

The more carefully you choose your words and phrases, the more effective your descriptions will be. Using precise language and content words can help build your vocabulary.

Using Precise Language

Using precise language is important in expressing exactly what you mean. For example, an author who writes "the snake *slithered* through the grass" gives a clearer—and more interesting—description of that action than an author who writes "the snake *moved* through the grass."

Words such as *slithered* and *moved* express action. When you choose an action verb, think about exactly what kind of information you want to give your readers or listeners. What do you want them to visualize? Study the verbs in each row below. Notice how each verb has a slightly different meaning. Visualize each action as you read.

eat	nibble	gobble	munch
cut	hack	split	trim
throw	heave	toss	hurl

Other words describe emotions or states of being. Study the words below. Notice how the choice of a word affects your idea of how someone might feel or act.

angry	annoyed	furious	irritated
lonely	distant	deserted	aloof
joyful	happy	thrilled	content

Now turn to page 291 to practice using precise language.

Name _____

Using Precise Language

Practice

Complete each sentence below with the word in parentheses that more *precisely* fits the sentence. Circle your answers.

1. Anne (raced, strolled) to catch the train before it left.

2. The teacher (asked, quizzed) us about last night's reading assignment.

3. The plate fell to the floor and (broke, shattered) into many little pieces.

4. "I'm sorry I borrowed your shirt without asking you," my sister (stammered, said).

5. The field was (damp, flooded) after three days of rain.

6. The baby (whined, complained) when the dog ran off with his toy.

7. The bird (took, snatched) the cracker from my hand when I was not looking.

8. Jake was (relieved, happy) when the dentist told him he had no cavities.

9. The puppy (ran, dashed) to the boy and scrambled into his lap.

10. The scientists (met, discovered) Native American pottery at the site.

11. Heather was (hungry, starving) after missing breakfast.

12. My friends were (talking, whispering) about me when I joined them.

Model: Using Content Words

You need to choose your words carefully when you are communicating about a particular topic. **Content words and phrases** are specific to a topic or course of study, and they give meaning to new concepts. For example, imagine you are discussing the topic of natural resources. You might use words such as *renewable, nonrenewable, biofuel, nuclear, solar, alternative, energy, hydropower,* and *environment* as you focus on this topic.

Think about how you use content words that are specific to each subject you study in school. For example, you learn in math class that the word *equivalent* means "equal" and that the word *percent* refers to one part of 100. In science class, you might learn that a *constellation* is a group of stars and that a *carnivore* is an animal that eats other animals. You read in social studies class that *export* means "to sell or carry goods to other countries" and that *import* means "to buy or bring goods into a country."

Take a Look → Using Content Words

Asking and answering questions is a strategy you can use to learn new words. When you come across an unfamiliar word, you might ask these questions: What is it? What are some of its properties? What is an example of it? If a text doesn't give you all of the information you need, you can use your own background knowledge or other reference materials to find the information. Read the following passage and apply this strategy to understand the word *ecosystem*.

> Ecosystems are nature's communities. What kind of an ecosystem do you live in? Do you live in a hot desert or in a leafy forest? Maybe you live on a frozen tundra or on open grassland. Wherever you live, you are part of an ecosystem. All healthy ecosystems are different, but they all work the same way. They are made up of living and nonliving parts that all work together.

ecosystem	
What is it?	the living and nonliving things that interact within a community
What are some of its properties?	All ecosystems have living and nonliving things. All ecosystems need space. Every ecosystem can be changed by its climate.
What is an example of it?	A desert, a forest, and a pond are examples of ecosystems.

Now turn to page 294 to practice using content words.

Name _____

Using Content Words

Practice

Read the passage below. Then use the strategy of asking and answering questions to help you better understand the highlighted words.

> **The cheetah is an animal in trouble.**
> Key factors have caused the cheetah to be listed as an **endangered** animal. Even though it is the fastest land mammal, it cannot always escape those who hunt it for its beautiful coat. Cheetahs thrive on open land where they can find lots of hoofed **wildlife** for prey. Humans have been taking over their habitat and turning it into farmland. However, there is hope for the cheetah's future. Several **conservation** organizations are working to save the cheetah from extinction.

endangered	
What is it?	
What are some of its properties?	
What is an example of it?	

Wildlife	
What is it?	
What are some of its properties?	
What is an example of it?	

Conservation	
What is it?	
What is an example of it?	
What are some of its properties?	